SO
LITTLE
DONE

Also by Theodore Dalrymple

If Symptoms Persist

SO LITTLE DONE

THE TESTAMENT OF A SERIAL KILLER

Theodore Dalrymple

ANDRE DEUTSCH

First published in Great Britain in 1995 by
Andre Deutsch Limited
106 Great Russell Street, London WC1B 3LJ

ISBN 0 233 98959 5

Printed in Great Britain by
WBC Bridgend

1

You hypocrites! You pretend (not only to others but even to yourselves) that you're reading this for a higher purpose, such as understanding the mind of a so-called serial killer like me. But why are you interested in the mind of a serial killer in the first place, may I ask? And what good would your understanding do you, even supposing it were attainable from reading what I have written? Would it prevent the emergence of a single such killer in the future, or facilitate his detection? No, it's not enlightenment you're after, but salacious entertainment; you'd be much more profitably employed on learning something of practical value, such as how to repair your central heating system. Go to the immersion heater, thou sluggard; consider its ways and be wise. (I have adapted very slightly a verse from *Proverbs* in the Bible, Chapter 6, verse 6, I believe, though it isn't easy to check in my present circumstances: I mention this only because I consider it the height of bad manners to make a literary allusion without disclosing its source to the reader.)

Cheap thrills and a *frisson* of excitement: that's what art is all about, when you strip it of its pretensions. It's prurience, after all, that keeps the cinema, the newspapers and literature going. The world has a lot to thank murderers for, when you come to think of it. Not that I expect gratitude, though my activities have stimulated something of a tourist boom in Eastham, a dismal town hitherto devoid of attractions, even (or perhaps especially) for its inhabitants. I understand I have provided employment for the manufacturers of souvenirs: for I am reliably informed that T-shirts with the legend *I visited Graham Underwood's house and survived* are on sale everywhere in the town.

According to the Italian newspapers, I am *Il Mostro di Eastham*: the Monster of Eastham. I'm learning Italian in prison, a beautiful and poetic language, and have managed to force the Prison Department to deliver *La Repubblica* to me every day, though it arrives a few days late, for no good reason that I can detect.

My feat of interring fifteen people in an urban garden hardly bigger than a graveyard plot – my life has been full of ironies – without having been found out by my self-righteous neighbours has caused wonderment throughout the world, and added immeasurably to the gaiety of the nation. People imagine they are being witty when they call me Graham Underground, and suppose they are the first to have thought of the joke. But how much greater would their admiration for me have been had it been generally known that I have successfully eliminated seven others, so successfully in fact that even after I had provided the police with the fullest possible details, it proved quite impossible to trace them.

Not that the police tried very hard, except to prevent knowledge of my subsidiary confession from leaking to the public, and thereby becoming a reproach to their negligence and incompetence. They pretended to believe, when I made my confession, that I was trying to mislead them at a time when the resources of their forensic laboratory were already overstretched by the fifteen cases whose bodies had already been found; besides, I overheard one police officer remark to another that the kind of person I had killed was the kind of person nobody missed, on whom it was hardly worth wasting a lot of time and effort. And these, ladies and gentlemen, are the men who present themselves as the guardians of public safety and morals, and who presume to stand in judgment over me!

I need hardly add that this was not the only instance of hypocrisy of which I was, and am, the victim. Two weeks after my arrest a journalist, dressed in a sharp double-breasted olive green suit and posing as a long-lost cousin, succeeded in visiting me in prison and offered me £1 million for the exclusive rights to my story. Naturally, he represented one of those cheap and sordid newspapers which campaign regularly for the execution of people such as I (I am punctilious in my insistence on the correct grammatical use of *I* and *me*, by the way): but only after they have written their memoirs to boost the flagging circulations of tabloid newspapers, of course.

As for the prisoners, they felt at liberty, indeed a moral compulsion, to attack me whenever they could, usually in packs of at least three just in case it should turn out that I was a karate champion. I was initiated into the ways of my fellow-inmates when five of them set upon me in the showers which the prison authorities, in the belief that everyone under arrest must also be infested with lice, have decreed that everyone remanded into their tender care from the courts should take on reception into it. 'You fucking nonce,' they – my fellow-inmates – repeated a hundred times (verbal invention not being a strong point of the criminal classes) as they kicked me black and blue while I lay defenceless on the shower room floor. The warders (or screws) turned a blind eye to these proceedings, because they approved of them.

A nonce, I discovered soon enough, is a sex offender; and in the moral hierarchy of the prisoner (if moral is quite the word I seek), even a cockroach is higher than a nonce. The authorities are delighted that the prisoners, or *cons* as they call them, have a hierarchy of their own – it helps them run the prisons, and I do not exaggerate

7

when I say that there's no one lazier in the world than a screw. So long as men have someone whom they can call their inferior, they are happy.

And why did the other prisoners consider me a nonce, I who have been described by several psychiatrists as completely lacking in sexual drive, indeed as entirely asexual? Because in their impoverished imagination the only reason anyone could have for killing fifteen people was to enjoy that momentary orgasmic gratification which played so large a part in their own miserable lives (and, I am led to believe, in the lives of almost everyone else). How many hours did they dream in their cells of this fleeting moment of sexual pleasure, how many hours did they pass speaking about it among themselves! They could not conceive of someone, such as I, who lived on an altogether higher, more intellectual, less instinctual plane.

But let us suppose for the sake of argument that it was for sexual reasons that I killed. Let us suppose also that at the moment of death of my so-called 'victims' I experienced that sudden release from desire which is the absurd and self-contradictory object of all desire. Would that have made me worthy of my fellow-prisoners' scorn, and given them the right to beat me up *ad libitum*? Would it not rather have exonerated me from all possible blame?

Which of us knows from where his sexual proclivities come, how they develop, how they are formed, what nourishes and sustains them? How, then, can anyone be held accountable for what excites him? And in any case, is not the proscription of certain sexual acts merely a matter of social convention? Homosexuality – for centuries vilified, condemned, outlawed and severely punished – was suddenly declared by fiat of parliament to be not so terrible after all, and rendered legally permissible at a stroke. But bestiality and necrophilia remain beyond the pale. Who suffers from these latter acts, however? The chickens, the corpses? No, they are forbidden still because someone in authority is personally repelled by them – which is usually a sign of secret attraction. Those who protest loudest are always unsure of themselves. There are parts of the world, after all, in which bestiality is so common as to be perfectly normal. And what about the incest taboo? What rational grounds can there be against incest in these times of a hundred different methods of contraception? The taboo is biologically necessary, we are told, to prevent the birth of the monstrous offspring of consanguinous parents: but what force does such an argument hold when a simple operation, much safer than any pregnancy and parturition itself, is available to rectify the failures of contraception? What is permitted and forbidden, ladies and gentlemen, is fundamentally a matter of taste – and power, of course.

Let us take these prisoners – the majority – who are so outraged by the crimes of nonces that they cannot refrain from assaulting them repeatedly. Let us compare them with, say, an imaginary man who is sexually aroused by the strangulation of old ladies in their nineties, and who has gratified himself in that direction on three separate occasions. Please note that it is not their crimes which we are now comparing, but the harm done by their respective sexual behaviour. Which of them is worse, the average prisoner or the strangler of old ladies?

The average prisoner, in case you don't know it, is an avid procreator of the species. But the care he takes of those whom he fathers is exiguous, both by choice and circumstance. Generally, he sees the mere fact of paternity as a proof of his potency, though his sperm count is something which is scarcely under his control. He has usually fathered children by at least two mothers, the more the better. He abandons such mothers with scarcely a thought, or beats them at will, or sometimes

9

both. It would never occur to him, not if he were to live to be a thousand years, to provide any of them with the necessities of life. And even if by some strange mischance he concerns himself with the fate of his children, he neverthless commits acts which are certain to lead to prolonged separation from them.

As for the women he selects, they are as fit for motherhood as fish for flight. You see them – those few who maintain contact with their so-called lovers – on their way to prison at visiting times, tarts all of them, tottering along on their absurd high heels, dressed in cheap and flimsy finery despite the cold, or in body-hugging lycra and multicoloured shell suits, their hair badly dyed with the roots showing their true colour, their faces vivid with a surfeit of cheap makeup, their figures kept unhealthily slender by the smoking of sixty cigarettes a day, or fattened by the incessant consumption of junk food. They drag their little children after them, smudge-faced and resisting, the girls prematurely slatterns, and the boys already fixed at the age of three with an expression of determined criminality upon their faces.

What is the future of these children, in all conscience? A life of pointless crises brought about by themselves, of cheap and damp lodgings whose furniture is impregnated with urine, of evictions and bailiffs, of domestic arguments and assaults, of drunkenness and nights in police cells, of poverty and a circle of misery spreading outwards from them like the ripples in a pond after a stone has been thrown into it.

All this is known – or at least, is knowable – in advance, yet the average prisoner not only has several children, but thinks he has done something fine and worthy in having them, and thirsts for more. He is the willing progenitor of lifetimes of torment.

Contrast this with the strangler of old ladies in their nineties. It is more than likely that the 'victims' are stricken with arthritis, unable to walk or even to rise from a chair unassisted, incontinent, partially blind and half-deaf. What value, then, does their life have for them? Probably they have begged their doctors many times to put them out of their misery. They are alive only because they cannot die by willpower alone. Death comes to them not as an enemy, but as a friend, long-awaited and heartily welcomed.

I am not so foolish as to deny that strangulation causes them some temporary fear and discomfort. I wish to be completely open and honest in this brief essay, unlike the defenders of the law and others who stand in authority over us. But few indeed are the modes of death which are completely without their moments of terror and discomfort. It is unlikely, therefore, that the old ladies would have shuffled off this mortal coil (*Hamlet*) entirely free of pain or discomfort; and strangulation is therefore not worse than what they would eventually have experienced in any case.

And so, if we draw up a balance sheet of the predictable suffering caused by the sexual activities of the average prisoner and the 'pervert' who derives pleasure from strangling old ladies, we must conclude that the suffering caused by the former is incomparably the greater than that caused by the latter. Indeed, the strangler might be said to be a benefactor of mankind, insofar as he reduces the sum of misery in it. The prisoner, of course, is to misery what compound interest is to money.

But how does the law and conventional morality distinguish between them? I need hardly ask you to imagine the fulminations in the press of which such a strangler would be the occasion. But the press passes over the procreative activities of the average prisoner in complete silence; and the law treats his right to recreate mayhem around him as absolutely sacrosanct, while condemning the strangler's proclivities in the strongest possible fashion.

11

2

You will have noticed by now that I can quote literature with facility, though I am not what you, with your conventional ideas, would probably call an educated man. I haven't been to university or any other institution of so-called higher learning, though that doesn't mean that I cannot think for myself. On the contrary.

It wasn't that I lacked the necessary ability for higher learning: only the opportunity. I am what is contemptuously known by those more favourably placed at birth as an autodidact, which is why (they allege) I take pleasure in long words and convuluted arguments. I have never been able, or rather allowed, to live up to my natural abilities: my voice has a nasal, suburban whine, and is too high-pitched. I grant that I am no Adonis and my posture leaves much to be desired, but above all my vowels are wrong. A man could be a genius in this country, but if he mispronounces his vowels he has no hope of success. It is speech which distinguishes Man from the animals, after all, and to be told that you don't speak properly is to be told something deeply wounding.

My father was a Scotsman. How or why he came to England I never discovered. The child may be father to the man, but we must not forget that the father is nevertheless the father to the child. And my father was violent, in or out of drink: my earliest memory is of him beating my mother, and then giving me a swipe – *en passant*, as it were, which hurled me across the room and into the wall – when I began to cry.

Then suddenly, when I was seven, he deserted us, and it is a measure of the confusion his desertion caused that I still cannot decide whether this was a good or a bad thing. At any rate, it meant that my mother had to provide for me, since there was no question of my father doing so. She went out to work, but having no skills to speak of she could take only menial employment. She worked for several years as an assistant in the kitchens of a local school (not even achieving the rank of cook), and there conceived such a strong dislike of children that she never spoke to me in anything but an exasperated shriek. I think she blamed me for my own existence, as if I had called myself into being without any participation on her part, and whenever she touched me, which was as few times as possible, it was as if she were handling something – some object – which was deeply distasteful and uncleanably dirty. Her inability or unwillingness to form any physical intimacy with me has affected me down to this day: I have never liked to be touched, and associate the sensation of two human skins in contact not with affection or pleasure, but with rejection and humiliation. I remember the violence with which she would seize my hand after I returned from school and try to remove the deeply ingrained blue ink from my fingers with a rough pumice stone. She said it was to keep me clean and respectable, but I think it was to inflict pain upon me for my unpardonable crime of having drawn breath.

She received no help from anybody, and we lived – hating one another – in a dismal, dark and damp little flat above a shop. The landlord, who was the greengrocer below, would shout abuse at us if the rent was as much as an hour overdue. She pretended that if it weren't for me, and my constant need for food, she would have been living a life of ease and luxury. When my shoes wore out because my feet had grown, and I needed a new pair, the sour look on her face told me that she

13

blamed me for my perverse tendency to grow, while her income remained the same. I wasn't allowed to ask my contemporaries at school to come home to play with me, in case they asked for something to eat. Not that I would have wished to subject any of them to my mother's embittered hospitality.

Whether or not I was solitary by nature, I soon enough became so. One grows into one's circumstances, as it were. If I found myself alone in the company of another child, I had nothing to say to him. The harder I thought of something to say, the less anything occurred to me. I was teased as an oddity, as someone who held himself aloof by choice, did not participate in games, and did not share in the adventure of smoking in the school bomb shelters (it was a full decade after the end of the War, but still they were not demolished). More than one child gained his spurs as a warrior by attacking me, usually at the instigation of a group of jeering bystanders. Even as a victim, however, I was contemptible, because I did not fight back in the expected way, which would have justified retrospectively the initial, unprovoked attack upon me. It is surprising how exhausting it is to hit an unresisting person (just as the body of a man feels heavier once the life has gone out of it), and my attackers soon gave up, slinking away unsatisfied by, and even disgusted with, my inertness. I did not alight upon this tactic by cunning or by deep reflection: it came to me naturally. I was no Christ figure, turning the other cheek (Matthew, chapter 5, verse 39), loving my enemies and doing good to those who hated me (Luke, chapter 6, verse 27). On the contrary, I conceived an absolute contempt for my tormentors who, it seemed to me, could do nothing of their own volition but had always to act in concert. Even my teachers, who should have been my protectors, sided with the other children because of my oddity, and made jokes about me in front of the whole class.

My pastimes were solitary, therefore: for a while I collected the numbers of buses or trains, spending long hours on bridges over roads or railway tracks and deriving real excitement from spying a locomotive or a bus which I had not previously seen. I wrote down the numbers in a little book which I have still (I admit that I am something of a hoarder). I had by then come to the conclusion that Man's artefacts were more to be relied upon, and were definitely more admirable, than Man (or rather Boy) himself, and I spent as much time as possible away from human company. I avoided my mother also, and she was happy enough for me to do so, though she pretended otherwise: her bitterness, her unceasing and unsparing criticism of me, the ill-grace with which she provided what little I had, encouraged me to lock myself away from her, a habit which then became the grounds for further criticism of me. 'You're becoming just like your father,' she would say. 'Why don't you speak to me? Or do you think I'm here just to provide your meals whenever you want them? Isn't it enough that I've ruined my life for you, without you being so sullen? Speak, child!' And she would hit me on the ear, as if conversation were money to be shaken out of a money box.

An ill-used or maltreated child dreams of his revenge upon the world, but his means are limited by his size and weakness. Friendless and alone, what could I have done to right the wrongs I suffered? It was at the age of eight that I discovered the joys of inflicting pain upon other living creatures. And who dare blame a child of that age for his cruelty, who not only lacks the capacity to understand the wellsprings of his actions, but has no one who cares about him sufficiently to correct him?

I caught flies and removed their wings for the pleasure of seeing their frantic but hopeless and unavailing struggles. The faint crisp sound made by their wings as I picked them off gave me an inexplicable thrill. It never occurred to me that the nervous systems of these insects

15

were too lowly on the evolutionary scale for them to suffer in any intelligible sense, but if such a thought had occurred to me it would have destroyed the purpose of the game. The arbitrariness and whimsicality of my actions (occasionally I would let a captured fly go) was what pleased me, and the exercise of power over another living being, which was a new experience for me.

I found beetles and turned them on to their backs, watching their legs kick to the point of exhaustion and immobility in their attempts to right themselves, which I ensured would not succeed. Then, using my finger nails as pincers, I picked off their legs one by one, thereafter turning the beetles right way up to 'discover' (as if I were conducting a scientific experiment in search of knowledge) how many legs a beetle needed to drag itself along. What an exquisite pleasure it was to watch the maimed insects trying to drag themselves to safety, in the knowledge that I could resume my 'experiment' at any moment I chose. That the beetle knew neither the cause nor the reason for what I supposed was its suffering was, of course, an additional joy to me.

I experimented in other ways. I immersed worms in water, but finding that, after an initial frenzy of squirming, they settled down and seemed content enough, and in any case survived longer in their new environment than my patience would bear, I added various substances such as salt or bleach to the water to make them lively again and finally disintegrate into vermicular slime. Quite often I persuaded myself that I acted from curiosity and not from cruelty: the faculties of self-deception and dishonesty being among the first of the human mind to develop. But could my self-imputed curiosity explain why I laughed for joy as I observed with minute attention the death-throes of my captives?

No living creature that came within my power was safe from my experiments. I put vinegar or acetone in fishbowls: how frenziedly fish die! Table salt placed on a

16

frog's moist skin was a superb experience. Ants were a constant source of delight: how easy it was to imagine that they were pests, and that, by pouring boiling water into the cracks in the ground from which they seemed to emanate in such numbers, one was actually performing a useful function!

One day I discovered by chance that warm eggs taken from birds' nests would hatch if kept warm in a jar filled with cotton wool. The fledgling suffocated: thenceforth I was not interested in the cold eggs of abandoned nests, beautiful as I found them, but only in the warm eggs of brooding birds which I frightened off their nests. Older now, my patience had increased, and I could watch my little jar for hours on end, in anticipation of the birth of the hapless fledgling, which would struggle blindly for air and then – slowly – expire by suffocation.

I should have liked to progress to cats and dogs, for I was becoming aware of the deficiencies of the lower animals as subjects for torture. But I realised also the difficulties involved: my mother had always refused to keep such an animal because of the unnecessary expense involved, and their capture was likely to prove difficult. They could bite and scratch: in short, fight back. I was not interested in a contest – my instincts were not at all sporting – but rather in the sure infliction of suffering without the least chance of escape. I knew that with cats and dogs the pleasures were in proportion to the risks, but I have never been a taker of risks. My one success with a cat was with an old, scarred and arthritic tom belonging to our neighbour, which would not have lived long in any case. I doused him in kerosene and set him alight. Old as he was, but impelled by the flames, he discovered reserves of both energy and agility. I had never seen such frenzy before, nor have I seen it since.

For the most part, however, I had to content myself – where cats and dogs were concerned – with the fights which arose between them spontaneously, the lure of which I never could resist. I loved to see the arched back of a cornered cat, its fur bristling; or to hear at night the unearthly screeches of two cats in dispute over their territory; or to see a large dog in the local park grip a smaller one by the throat with its teeth and shake it like a rat. But in the last analysis, these fights always disappointed me: firstly because the owners of the dogs would separate them, or the cats would desist before killing one another, but secondly, and more importantly, because they did not fall within my power. There was no revenge upon the world, no assuaging of my humiliation, in suffering and injury not inflicted by the exercise of my own will.

I mention my childish cruelties in the interests of truth: I do not wish to present myself as a born saint.

But you will still condemn me: a monster, you will exclaim in a rush of self-righteousness, a congenital pervert! But I repeat, my cruelty was the natural, indeed the inevitable, outcome of my upbringing, which I did nothing to choose for myself. And even if cruelty were part of my essential nature, which it needed only a certain environment to germinate, who would be to blame for it? A man is born into this world as helpless as the fledgling in my bottle.

Look to yourselves, I say! Are you quite sure you do not countenance cruelty on vastly greater scale than ever mine was, and all the more reprehensible because you could put an end to it if you so wished?

I see that a puzzled expression spreads over your face, a look of offended innocence. You grow angry: how dare he compare himself with us, who love our pets and send donations to the RSPCA! Has he no shame?

But, ladies and gentlemen, you eat meat, you drink milk, you consume eggs. It does not matter whether or not you know how these commodities are produced: for if you do not know, your ignorance is wilful and therefore culpable. I am not speaking now of the com-

18

parative handful of lower animals which – as I now realise – were incapable of the suffering which I attributed to them, but rather I am speaking of the untold millions of sentient beings which are maintained in unspeakable conditions, just so that you might afford their meat or other produce. Am I mistaken in recalling that at the time of my childhood, chicken was still a luxury food, which my mother put on the table but once or twice a year, and then only to demonstrate the extent of her martyrdom? Who now remembers the days, which after all were not so very long ago, when to eat chicken once a week was a sign of prosperity?

And what, I ask you, do you suppose has brought about the transformation of chicken from a luxury food into the meat of the masses? Cruelty, of course. I do not mean that the principal object of the modern chicken farmer (a profession to which Himmler gave a bad name) is the deliberate maltreatment of these foolish and in some ways unattractive, but nonetheless sentient, birds. By all means let us not overstate the case by falsely claiming that these creatures are capable of the highest processes of thought or the most refined of sentiments. But I still maintain that for avian flesh to be so widely available, within the budget of all, cruel means of raising it are imperative. And who wishes the end wishes the (inescapable) means.

I presume I do not have to describe in any detail a modern battery chicken farm to establish my point. Let me mention merely the tiny cages in which the unfortunate birds spend their entire lives, so small indeed that there is not enough room in them for the birds to turn round or move in any direction whatever; and let me mention also that the birds are so immobile that their feet grow round the wire mesh below them, and become so intrinsic a part of the cage itself that when the time comes for the removal of the birds from their cages their feet have to be cut from under them while they are still

19

alive. Needless to add, the separation of a chicken from its feet is performed without anaesthetic: you wouldn't like contaminated flesh, and in any case the government wouldn't permit it.

The other meat which you so thoughtlessly consume every day is likewise the product of cruelty. Only your desire to continue dining in peace of mind prevents you from enquiring into the conditions of your local abattoir, conditions which you would pharisaically claim to horrify you if you were presented with inescapable evidence of their existence, and which you dimly apprehend but from which you delicately avert your gaze. You are the Pontius Pilates of meat-eating.

At least as a child I had the courage of my cruelty. Unlike you, I did not depute it to others to commit on my behalf, that I might claim to be an animal lover. I did what I had to do myself, and never imagined that suffering inflicted behind a veil of secrecy ceased to be suffering.

I have renounced completely my former cruelty to animals, and have become a strict vegetarian. I also wear plastic shoes, though I permit myself wool, because it does not necessitate the slaughter of sheep which, moreover, are still kept in fields. When sheep are factory-farmed I shall renounce the use of wool.

In this respect, I am vastly your moral superior. I no longer form part of that self-satisfied majority at whose implicit and silent, but nevertheless imperious, behest numberless atrocities against defenceless animals are committed throughout the land – a land of people who burst into tears at the sight of a puppy with its paw in plaster, and who give large sums of money to support a trauma unit for injured hedgehogs!

I need hardly add that the screws – men who personify roast beef and plenty of beer, and who for the most part did not join the prison service from the love of their fellow men – found my vegan diet and convictions a matter for derision. (Eggs and milk are produced in this society under conditions which are not acceptable to me.) The screws and other prisoners considered it funny to hide meat in my vegetables, and when I protested they replied, 'Sorry, we thought you was a cannibal, Underwood!' And I had to threaten court action to obtain the vitamin supplements which the atrocious diet provided for vegans in prison makes a matter of necessity, not mere preference. The prison authorities thought that if they half-starved me, I should give up my diet and become a normal meat-eater again. They little knew with whom they had to deal, or what it is to have fixed moral principles.

But why, you may ask, did they try so hard to reconvert me to a carnivorous existence? The provision of a complete vegan diet for me was not, after all, a difficult matter. I know the answer, however: because they themselves knew in their heart of hearts that I was right and they were wrong. And how could these pillars of the law allow themselves to be the moral inferiors of *Il Mostro di Eastham*?

3

No, ladies and gentlemen, I am not a cruel man. The police found no signs of torture on the bodies of what both you and they are pleased to call my 'victims'. Of course, they lost no time in explaining this mysterious and to them incomprehensible absence by the advanced state of decomposition of the cadavers. But with such paltry arguments they could have proved anything they liked: and I need hardly allude to the growing propensity of the police to concoct their evidence, and not just their arguments. If it were not for the fact that I freely admit to my 'crimes', indeed that I proudly avow them, you would not be absolutely certain that I was the author of them, insofar as the administration of our so-called justice system has come to such a pass that any verdict of guilty arouses (quite rightly) as many doubts as it settles. And it should be borne in mind that even so I am guilty only in the formal, or juridical, sense of the word, not in the much more important moral sense, which so very few in our society understand.

Another thing which puzzled the police, with their defective and impoverished imaginations, was the fact that my 'victims' (it would be tiresome not to use the accepted, if entirely misconceived, designation) were of both sexes and of many, if not quite all, ages. In the past, killers of more than one person – who is usually the wife – specialised, as it were: that is to say, they killed only prostitutes, young children or homosexual lovers. The sexual motive of the killings has generally been obvious, even to the slow understanding of the police. And therefore in my case the police, assuming that whatever was the motive in the past must be the motive in the present and the future, have publicly stated that I was 'a polymorphously perverse sadist' (one can just imagine how proud the semi-literates of the force were of that polysyllabic and grandiloquent phrase). Naturally, I took immediate steps to defend my reputation: I instructed my lawyer to file a suit for libel. Of course, it wasn't only my reputation I was concerned to protect: there was an important matter of principle at stake, namely that the authorities should not be at liberty gratuitously to denigrate citizens. The case did not even reach the courts, however, because the police climbed down, issued a public apology and offered me a payment which I donated to charity. I have always acted in the public interest.

Then they sent in the psychiatrists, to pluck out the heart of my mystery, as Hamlet remarked to Guildenstern (or was it Rosencrantz? You will understand that it is not always easy to check one's sources in my present circumstances.) There were four of them, two for the prosecution and two for the defence. Convinced of my own sanity, I had not asked for any such examinations, but my lawyer persuaded me that, since I was defended at public expense, I had nothing to lose by such examinations and no stone should remain unturned. We did not have to disclose the reports of the psychiatrists hired to defend me, should they prove unfavourable to my case, and therefore it was best to cooperate with them.

Nothing to lose, said my lawyer: oh, but there was, there was. It had always been my intention to write an explanation and defence of my activities, which are so easily misunderstood, and I flatter myself that my story is not without points of interest. But I found that I had to repeat my life history, in precisely the same form, to four psychiatrists in quick succession, and there is

23

nothing quite like repetition for removing the freshness from a narrative.

And of what does the supposed science of psychiatry consist, in any case? At best it is the mutton of platitude dressed up as the lamb of profundity. In its parlance, a man does the things he does because of his character. And how does it know what kind of character a man has? Because of the things he does. This, in a nutshell, is the whole science of psychiatry.

Judges listen to this nonsense, of course, and accord it deep respect. Knowing nothing of life, indeed protected from it by the elaborate and pompous ceremonial with which they are surrounded, they are perfect fools: that is, when they are not perverts themselves, like a Lord Chief Justice of the recent past who was reputed to have had an orgasm each time he passed the death sentence.

It is well-known that psychiatrists are not the most balanced of people themselves, yet they presume to judge the sanity of others. And what a procession of the intellectually halt, limping and lame passed before me in the name of psychiatric science! One of them, dressed in a corduroy jacket and open necked shirt (very unprofessional) spoke in exaggeratedly dulcet tones, as if to imply that he would understand anything I said to him, and that his understanding was a form of infallible absolution. I had the distinct impression that another of them, younger than the rest but already balding, was excited, and perhaps even honoured, to be called upon to examine a personage as notorious as I, whose conduct had preoccupied the newspapers for days on end. He looked at me as though he were searching for visible signs of wickedness upon my countenance, but he asked the same foolish questions as all the others, that I might fit into the procrustean psychiatric moral and diagnostic schemata. In particular, they were interested in whether I heard voices.

'Of course I hear voices,' I said. 'I'm not deaf. Don't you hear voices?'

'I mean, do you hear voices when you're on your own?'

It was clear from this question that these psychiatric gentlemen had no conception of what prison life is like. You are never alone in prison. Even a celebrated professor (you could tell his academic rank from the electric blue bow tie he wore, which no one else would have dared to wear), who had devoted his entire life to the study of criminals and prisoners, asked this inane question.

'At night,' I replied, 'when I am alone in my cell, I hear hundreds of voices. They keep me awake, in fact. Prisoners are very noisy.'

'No,' said the psychiatrists, one and all. 'I mean when there is no one there.'

'If I heard voices, I'd assume there was somebody there, wouldn't I?'

'Well, have you ever heard voices and been surprised to discover that there wasn't anyone there?'

'Unfortunately, my present circumstances are not conducive to an extensive search for the source of the noises which I hear.'

They expressed a consistent interest also in whether I thought there was anyone against me.

'The five million readers – if that is quite the word for them – of *The Sun* newspaper, for a start,' I replied. 'It has run a campaign protesting against the luxurious conditions in which it alleges I am held. I hear there has been an impressive postal response to its campaign, unprecedented in fact, suggesting a variety of punishments for me, mostly involving surgery without anaesthetic. Yes, I think there are people against me.'

All the psychiatrists said that they had meant whether I thought there was anyone *in particular* against me, any individual as such.

'The crown prosecutor,' I suggested.

They hadn't meant him, either. They meant, did I consider that there was a plot against me?

Lord, what fools these mortals be! (*A Midsummer Night's Dream*, Act 3, scene 2.) I had merely relayed to them what was common knowledge, obtainable from any newspaper: namely, that the dossiers on my case – or more properly, *cases* – were so extensive that they filled five rooms, that ten prosecutors, aided by two clerks each, were engaged full time upon them, and that for the time being the police forensic laboratories of an eighth of the entire country were accepting no work on cases other than mine. And if that did not constitute a plot against me, I didn't know what would have done so.

No, it wasn't *that* kind of plot the psychiatrists were talking about either, they said. One of them lost his temper and began to play the outraged citizen: how could I call it a plot against me, when all they were trying to do was discover the truth about the bodies in my back garden? He even suspected that I was being flippant, on a subject upon which humour was not only deeply misplaced but profoundly distasteful.

Well, I replied, the July plot against Hitler may have been fully justified, but it was still a plot.

And didn't I realise, asked the psychiatrist, who by now had turned the shade of purple which I suppose writers of letters to *The Daily Telegraph* turn as they pen their immortal thoughts on how criminals ought to be more severely punished, that I had cost the taxpayer not thousands, not tens of thousands, but hundreds of thousands and possibly even millions of pounds? The orchid in his buttonhole (he was the flamboyant type in a green tweed suit) fairly shook with indignation as he thought of it.

On the contrary, I replied. It was not I who had asked the police to dig about in my garden, or to instigate an investigation at such huge public expense. It was therefore the police who had put the public to it, not I: for was it not a time-honoured principle of English law that each man is deemed to be the author of his own acts and therefore responsible for their foreseeable consequences? Besides, the financial balance of my activities was clearly to the advantage of the taxpayer – but that is a question into which I shall go more deeply at a later stage.

In one of the reports written by these charlatans, there appears the following sentence:

> Mr Underwood [with what unctuous pedantry they all prefaced my name by *Mr*, to maintain the fiction that a man is presumed innocent until proven guilty, and to differentiate themselves from the whole penal apparatus, from which, however, they derived a handsome income] compensates for his deep sense of inferiority by insisting upon winning verbal victories.

I suppose, then, that the learned author of these words compensates for his deep sense of superiority by insisting on suffering verbal defeats!

But at least all the psychiatrists recognised my intelligence, I'll say that for them, though they couldn't quite bring themselves to admit that I was not merely intelligent, but highly intelligent. No, the best they could manage was *Mr Underwood appears to be of at least average intelligence*, which is damning with faint praise to say the least of it, when one considers what average intelligence is like.

And they conceded also – at my insistence – that I had never been employed in a capacity commensurate with my talents and abilities, though they took back with one hand what they granted with the other, through the use of the condescending phrase *Mr Underwood feels that*, as if the injustice under which I have laboured all my life were a matter of mere opinion and not of palpable fact, and as if I were incapable of distinguishing between fantasy and reality. Did not my mother say to me in flesh and blood reality, not in my overheated or psychotic imagination, that I was not to dream of continuing my education beyond the age at which it might legally cease, however good my results at school might be, because she was not prepared to support me after the age at which it was possible for me to find a job, and because she had already sacrificed more than enough years of her life to my welfare? I was fourteen years old at the time, my native intelligence had overcome the effects of an unhappy home life, I was top of my class and thinking of a career in a learned profession to which I would have been very well-suited. Yet on mature reflection, can one really blame her for her narrowness of mind when she worked for such meagre wages while others lived off the fat of the land? Why were her wages so small? Because those of others were so large, and she knew it. Thus was the injustice of our society transmitted to me via my mother: while some succeeded in life merely by virtue of having been born into the right families, others – such as I – were denied all opportunity and thus condemned to perform menial tasks for the rest of our lives.

But why, I hear some of you ask in your plummy and complacent middle-class voices, why couldn't he have gone to evening classes or to a college of further education, if he wanted to better himself and find more satisfying work? To which I reply: do you know of a single person who has used this route to success, among all your friends and acquaintances for example? No, you who have gone through life like a hot knife through butter don't understand, and don't wish to understand, how difficult it is to recover after failing – or rather, being failed – at the first hurdle of life's race. To return after a day's work to the miserable accommodation which society provides for such as I (in a neighbourhood in which the most ruthlessly antisocial person sets the tone and rules the roost, if I may be allowed for once to

28

mix my metaphor) is not conducive to strenuous efforts at self-improvement: on the contrary, it is a standing invitation to go to seed.

Nevertheless, I *did* improve myself, though not in ways of which this materialistic and diploma-crazed society would approve, or for which it would reward me financially. I spent every hour available to me in the public library, reading philosophy, history and literature – matters which lead nowhere as far as a career in this philistine country is concerned, but knowledge of which is essential to a cultured man.

But if you had energy for that, I hear some of you asking again, why not for accountancy or computing, which would have opened up real career prospects to you? To which I reply: can a man help being interested in those things which interest him (in my case, the Truth)? Does a man say to himself, henceforth I shall be interested in accountancy, and lo! henceforth he is interested in it? No, ladies and gentlemen, when a man has to struggle just to keep himself fed, housed and clothed, as I have had to do all my life, he cannot afford to use the fraction of energy remaining to him to study what is repugnant to him: and I am not a man, in any case, to compromise on matters of principle.

The psychiatrists admitted as much in their reports about me, but as usual made a vice of a virtue. They claimed that what they delicately called my *activities* were the result of a confluence of three circumstances or conditions: first that I was consumed with resentment because of my upbringing and the subsequent course of my life, second that I was an autodidact and therefore not trained or able to discern the validity of an argument, with a tendency to accept uncritically what I had read, and third that the rigidity of my character led me actually to act upon the principles which I came to accept.

To the charge of resentment, I plead justification.

As to my supposed inability to discern the validity or

otherwise of an argument, an inability which supposedly derives from my lack of formal education, it is so absurd a charge as to require no refutation. Do they suppose, these psychiatrists and so-called experts on the mind, that I read nothing in the public library with which I did not agree, or accept as true and valid? I read the materialists and the idealists, the Utilitarians and the Marxists, the divines and the atheists: how could I accept them all without making a choice between them when their arguments were so opposed to one another? A logical impossibility, even for such a one as I, who am untrained in argument. But these gentlemen with so many degrees and diplomas to their names that they cannot sign themselves on a single line imagine that a plain contradiction is invisible to anyone lacking such an alphabet soup after his name: otherwise, they might have to admit to themselves that they had wasted their lives in pointless and arid academic exercises. Did Shakespeare have any of their precious degrees, I ask you? Would anyone dare to say of him that, being an autodidact, he was neither trained nor able to discern the validity of an argument? Would he have been a greater writer had he been William Shakespeare M.D., Ph.D?

And finally to the most serious of all the charges against me, namely that I acted upon my principles. It isn't difficult to imagine what these psychiatrists would have written had I acted against my professed principles, or upon no principles at all: that I was a conscienceless psychopath (though such a description would have explained nothing, except to their satisfaction). Yet so hypocritical is the world they inhabit that they find it deeply disturbing when a man like me acts upon his principles in defiance of convention. Indeed, it becomes a matter of pathology for them.

Supposing I had acted in accordance with the dictates of convention, and allowed my fifteen (or twenty-two) 'victims' to continue living. How could I have reconciled

30

such inactivity on my part with my conscience? I could not have quieted it by telling myself that I was only obeying the law: that argument was successfully disposed of at Nuremberg, albeit with the usual inconsistencies which characterise the behaviour of constituted authority. Every man must work out for himself how he should act: he cannot hide behind laws, social conventions or the orders of others. The denial of personal responsibility leads to the most terrible consequences, as the history of our century has all too clearly demonstrated.

But the law which I broke, you protest, was a good law, a law necessary for the proper ordering of society. Moreover, it is one of the Ten Commandments (the sixth, in fact, being found in Exodus Chapter 20, verse 1): Thou shalt not kill.

And with this argument, you assume that the matter is now settled: I am guilty and should therefore be punished with such rigour as the law prescribes. But the matter is *not* settled, far from it: and I have much to say that will discomfit you, providing that you are not utterly incapable of overcoming those prejudices which the majority of mankind mistakes for principles.

I shall do you the honour of presuming that you are not a Tolstoyan pacifist, for surely it is an evil policy not to resist evil: in the contest between non-resistance and evil itself, the latter always emerges victorious. And, as I have said before, who wills the means, wills the end.

So I may take it that you have conceded that violence, including the taking of life, may sometimes be justified. There is such a thing, after all, as a just war. The last great world conflagration was precisely such a war: and had I been alive to see it, I should have been both honoured to fight and willing to sacrifice my life. And if I had killed fifteen (or twenty-two) then rather than now, I should have been accounted a hero rather than a villain. Even if I had killed twenty-two thousand, by dropping bombs on German cities and immolating the innocent

31

along with the guilty, I should not have been reproached, or expected to reproach myself, as a criminal.

How, I ask, is a person transformed from a citizen with the normal legal obligations into a licensed killer – a killer, moreover, who is praised in proportion to the number of fellow beings whom he kills? The transformation cannot be effected merely by the fiat of the government of the country in which he happens to live, which declares war and orders him to kill: for that way Nuremberg lies.

Nor can it be because the government which declares war is democratically elected or is so popular that it embodies the general will of the people. Did not the Nazi government fulfil both these criteria? Yet if Nuremberg erred, who can doubt that it was on the side of leniency, and because a third of the judges represented a regime and jurisdiction as steeped in blood as that of the Nazis?

There remains one possibility alone, therefore, to explain the legitimacy of the transformation of normal citizen into approved killer: that one may legitimately become such a killer when, and only when, one judges it right to do so. And this being the case, one may reasonably ask why it is right to kill only in war and not at other times: does an act become permissible merely because of its prevalence at the time? The fact that in wartime one acts with the *imprimatur*, as it were, of a government neither adds to nor detracts from one's personal responsibility for one's acts, as I have demonstrated. Neither can the fact that in war one's 'victims' are entirely foreigners alter the case, unless human life is to be valued according to its country of origin, a view which mankind has at long last, after centuries of immolation, rejected.

No, ladies and gentlemen, the conclusion is inescapable: one may be an ethical murderer. And I was one such.

32

4

I come now to yet another instance of the hypocrisy by which we are surrounded in this society as much as we are surrounded by oxygen in the atmosphere, though it would take a moral Lavoisier to discern it (I have read in the history of the sciences as well as in political and social history). It is this hypocrisy which has given rise to the excessive public interest in my case to which I have already alluded, an excess all the more striking when one considers that this same public has been unaware until now of nearly a third of my fatalities.

Shouldn't the interest a rational man expresses in a subject be proportional to the importance of that subject? Is this not a moral as well as an intellectual imperative? So that even if my activities were reprehensible in themselves (an hypothesis I entertain temporarily only for the sake of argument, and therefore not to be taken as an admission of blameworthiness) they were of no account, they were trivial even, set against the frightful events from around the world of which we receive news every day of the year, without fail.

But these events are very distant, you protest, and affect us not at all. To which I reply:

i) The moral significance of events is not proportional to their proximity to us, or inversely proportional to their distance.

ii) No man is an island (a hackneyed quotation, perhaps, from Donne's *Meditation XVII* from his *Devotions upon Emergent Occasions*, but appropriate

33

to my argument nonetheless). Therefore, send not to seek in whom the blame lies: it lies in thee.

iii) You were not in any case directly affected by my activities.

But I am getting ahead of myself. It is essential to establish certain important points, such as that the first three of my fifteen killings now known to the public took place so long ago – more than twenty years, in fact – that I have even forgotten the names of the so-called 'victims'. These the police are now making every effort to discover. But to what purpose, I ask? I selected my 'victims' with some care, as I shall in due course relate, but even supposing I made some mistakes in the selection process, and chose persons who were highly esteemed or even loved by their relatives, who have long wondered what became of them, it surely cannot serve anyone's interest that the names of these three now be revealed. Why open old wounds?

When I remarked to the detective who first interrogated me after the unlucky discovery of the human remains in my garden (if that is the right word for the mere handkerchief of land behind the terraced house which, on my miserable salary, it was formerly my life's work to purchase), that it was not worth his while to enquire after the oldest of the remains because the events which led up to their deposition were now so long ago, he was outraged – or at least, he affected outrage. I should not have said he was a man of deep or quick sensibility: he had that kind of solid fatness (common to plain clothes policemen and prison warders, though between the two professions no love is lost, each regarding the other as a form of low life) which is indicative of great strength in short bursts, such as is necessary for the beating up of a suspect, while it results in breathlessness, much sweating and even a heart attack when exertion over a longer period is required.

34

For the most part, however, the detective adopted that tone of sweet, even sickly, reasonableness which fundamentally cruel, aggressive and cynical people adopt when they are trying to be (or rather, to appear) kind. He pretended that we were equals, engaged upon an exciting voyage of discovery into the past, striving for academic reasons to uncover the truth of what happened. He did not mention the life sentence (in the absence of the death penalty) which he hoped would be my reward for my cooperation, and he called me by my first name immediately on meeting me, insisting that I also call him Bob. One could almost hear the police manual of interrogation speaking through him. When he offered me sandwiches, for example, he asked what filling I should like.

Is this the moment to ask who exactly was harmed by my activities? It is, of course, the philosophical, not the practical, question which I ask.

I have already implied that my 'victims' (though I should have preferred the word *beneficiaries*, had not the use of such a word in this context risked so alienating readers that they would refuse to read any further) were without relatives or friends to mourn the loss. I did my pre-event research thoroughly: one or two of the 'victims', it is true, may have had relatives still living, but such were their relations with them that their deaths (or disappearances, as it appeared at the time) were a cause more for celebration than for sorrow. One or two were the mothers of babies, but they were too young to mourn. Moreover, coming from that particular social *milieu*, which I shall in due course describe, the babies were destined for a life of such utter misery that, prevention being better than cure, I extinguished their lives also. No, the relatives of my 'victims' decidedly did not suffer from their deaths.

Who, then, suffered? The rest of society? I shall prove that this was far from having been the case: indeed, the exact opposite was nearer the truth. For the moment, I ask merely that you believe me, or rather suspend your disbelief, as the Athenian philosopher Aristotle (384–322 BC) put it: for have I not so far proved many things to you which you would not previously have believed?

This leaves but one candidate for the person or persons who were supposedly harmed by my activities: the 'victims' themselves. No doubt this is perfectly obvious to those of you, my readers, who have never read any philosophy. A great wrong, you all too easily suppose, must be done to his subject by a murderer.

But philosophy is the systematic examination of our unthinking prejudices. Let us, therefore, examine the question a little more closely.

There is a long tradition of welcoming death as a positive good: call no man happy, said the lawgiver Solon, till he dies, he is at best fortunate. (In any case, my 'victims' were not even fortunate.) And Francis Bacon, who achieved more philosophical detachment in his *Essays* than in his shady financial dealings, wrote famously of the absurdity of the fear of death. 'Men fear death as children fear to go in the dark,' he said. Not for nothing, ladies and gentlemen, did I spend the evenings (and the Saturdays) of twenty years of my life in the public library.

But it is not to the Ancients that I look to justify myself, excellent though they may have been. I look to the moderns: there is, after all, such a thing as progress, even in philosophy.

And it is the unanimous conclusion of all the best modern philosophers that the fear of death is at best a confusion, at worst a logical impossibility and therefore literally meaningless. Please note that I am not here appealing to authority to establish my conclusion: I am most emphatically not saying that something is so because those philosophers who are generally deemed by their colleagues, by *cognoscenti* and prizegivers etc., to be the best in the field have said it is so. On the contrary, I have read them myself and come to the conclusion, by my own ratiocination, that their arguments are conclusive.

And what they, and I, have to say about the fear of death is this: assuming that Man is possessed of no eternal soul which survives beyond his earthly end, his death is but oblivion or rather non-being: his consciousness is utterly extinguished. Now when people say they fear death, the image they have in their minds is that of a long, indeed endless, dark night of the soul. They imagine themselves buried alive, perhaps, frustrated by an inability to speak or otherwise communicate with those they have loved. Death is for them a deprivation of the senses, but with a continuation of the consciousness. But of course, after death there is no consciousness to be deprived of sense experience, such as having breakfast or receiving a written warning for alleged misconduct in the office (of which I received several, though I succeeded in having them withdrawn, and on two occasions extracted written apologies from my accusers, which I had framed and placed upon my desk). Thus to fear death is to fall into complete incoherence: you literally do not know what you are talking about, and it makes no more sense to ask what death is like than to ask what it was like before birth (or conception, if you prefer). Non-being is not an experience, and therefore cannot be feared.

But, you object, whether the notion is incoherent or not, fear of death is almost universal, except among the truly suicidal. No, I reply, it isn't death which is feared, but dying – the process itself. Everyone knows of people whose dissolution has come about in an undignified and painful way. And since death is inevitable, surely it is a consummation devoutly to be wished (*Hamlet* again) that we should die suddenly, and very nearly painlessly?

With these incontestable arguments in our minds, let us now turn to the alleged harm done to my 'victims'. Being dead cannot be a loss to them, since there is no one who exists who could be the subject of that supposed loss. I agree that the process of strangulation was a harm done them, but only a very slight one because they were destined (as are we all) to die anyway. Even had I tortured them to death, which I emphatically deny having done, I could hardly have done so for very long, indeed for only an insignificant portion of their lives (compare this with the ravages of chronic disease). In fact, I disposed of them humanely, more humanely than they deserved – as we shall see in due course. I spiked their drinks, they fell asleep peacefully and I strangled them. They knew neither fear nor suffering, and it was a death such as I could have wished for myself.

Indeed, I justly consider myself their benefactor. Most of them were heavy smokers, and at least some of whom would have contracted lung cancer eventually, or the other painful and debilitating diseases which are the natural consequence of that disgusting and antisocial habit which, incidentally (but not coincidentally) is universal amongst my fellow-prisoners. Others of my 'victims' – I am referring now especially to the women – had led notoriously promiscuous lives since an early age and would probably have died of one of the cancers associated with that way of life: a painful and lingering death. Yet others of my 'victims' were drunks, their livers already rotted by drink, so that one day they would have vomited blood like a dark red fountain (medicine was another interest of mine, and unlike most doctors, including my own, I have read one of the large textbooks – *Cecil and Loeb*, one thousand seven hundred and twenty three pages in the seventeenth edition, excluding the index – from cover to cover). From all these terrible deaths I preserved my 'victims'.

Our non-being lasts an eternity, literally an infinity of

time. Hence, to bring it forward by a few years is not to increase its length: infinity plus one still being infinity.

I have reduced you now to the arguments of desperation, the kind of argument in which our less cerebral newspapers frequently indulge, in order to produce a pleasant *frisson* of outrage in their readers: namely, that I not only killed my 'victims' but 'desecrated' their bodies. I cut them up and put them without ceremony into a common fossa.

How else, I ask you, was I supposed to dispose of them? My garden, as I have already informed you, was not exactly an estate. Some dismemberment was inevitable, in the circumstances. I derived no satisfaction from it, let alone thrill or sexual gratification: it was a job to be done, and an unpleasant one at that.

But this is not to go to the philosophical heart of the question. Again I ask: who was harmed by the so-called 'desecration' of the bodies? I blunted several knives beyond possibility of resharpening, for the human body is tough (a fact which has saved many a doctor from the consequences of his own incompetence), especially after death; but though several knives can said to have been harmed in the process, this is not a harm which counts in the moral sense. Yet the bodies were objects as inanimate as the knives themselves. It was no longer possible to harm the persons to whom they once belonged, the temple of whose souls they once were, or however else you might wish to put it. And since no one claimed the bodies either, since my 'victims' were selected precisely for their lack of close contact with others, I damaged no one's property. The alleged 'desecration' therefore turns out, on philosophical examination, to be nothing more serious than a breach of what you consider good taste. But again I say, *De gustibus non est disputandum*. (Surely it isn't necessary to translate?)

If, then, we look at my actions from the purely rational

standpoint, it can be seen that they were wholly without ill-effects. I explained as much to the interrogating detective, who was utterly baffled and unable to answer me on the philosophical plane, because he had spent his evenings in the pub chatting inconsequentially with his mates rather than in the public library. To much of what I said he replied not a word, so beyond dispute was its truth. I advised him to devote his working hours and such talents as he possessed to the solution of crimes whose victims (without the need this time for inverted commas) were still living and therefore capable of suffering from the effects of the offences committed against them. Was he not aware, I asked him, that only a third of all crimes were reported to the police, and that this was because so few criminals were caught that the average citizen no longer considered it worthwhile even to report the crimes committed against him? Instead of wasting his time on me, therefore, he would be better employed elsewhere: that is, if he had any compassion at all for the real, the true victims of crime.

5

I realise that I have strayed slightly from what I had intended to say.

The interest excited by my case (though I find it difficult to think of myself as a mere *case*, as surely anyone would), not only in this country but around the world, seemed to me excessive, to say the least. Some commentators have even suggested that I acted as I did specifically to court publicity, a fatuous suggestion which goes against the most elementary reasoning, when you consider that I concealed the material results of my activities for many years, a fact which other commentators, slightly more perspicaciously, have taken as evidence of my extreme cleverness, or cunning as they disparagingly put it. No, ladies and gentlemen, I have never been a publicity-seeker, and would have been content to carry on my work for ever in private, without acknowledgement.

Your work! you exclaim. I shall explain further when the time comes, for now I must ask you to have a little patience.

No sooner were the remains discovered quite by accident – my neighbour's sewer had flooded and the work to repair it strayed into my garden, without my permission I hasten to add, and I'm thinking of suing the water board – than an entire circus descended on Mandela Road (the council had changed its name from Waterloo Road only the month before). Floodlights blazed by night and the neighbours complained that they could get no sleep: they did not see the urgency of the work in any case, considering that many of the 'victims' had been dead for decades and were hardly to be resurrected. The digging went on twenty-four hours a day, while around the corner large vehicles containing generators for the arc lights needed by the television cameras made a continuous low grinding noise (so I am told: I wasn't there to hear it). Bulletins were issued every hour throughout the day, read to the press by a policewoman who tried to sound well-educated, or at least well-spoken, but who stumbled over long words, dropped her aitches and inserted them where they did not belong. Whom was she trying to fool? Everyone knows that the police are uncouth and ungifted intellectually, and the use of a few long words will not change matters.

Reporters besieged the entire neighbourhood. They stood vigil outside the homes of my neighbours, or of anyone who they thought might have some knowledge of me, however slight or inconsequential. Those who did not wish to speak to them (very few, considering the poverty of the neighbourhood and the blandishments which the gentlemen of the press were able to offer) were chased down the road whenever they ventured forth. A few stalwarts tried to escape the attentions of the fourth estate by leaving their houses via their back gardens: but the public guardians of truth soon caught on, and staked out the rear of the houses as well as their front.

In general, however, the neighbours were only too eager to oblige, if necesssary with pure fiction. Mr Aziz, the owner of the nearby corner shop, who until then had been only too happy to accept my custom, pretended that he knew all along that I had been a criminal, and alleged that I had been a shoplifter (the worst crime of which his avaricious *petit bourgeois* soul was able to conceive) as well as a multiple murderer. This was the rankest ingratitude, since the turnover of his miserable little shop tripled after my arrest, at least for a while. And then a kind of informal competition emerged in my street, to discover – for the benefit of reporters – who had discerned the most disgusting traits in my character, and who had discerned them earliest and therefore most presciently. My neighbours thought (probably not without reason) that the more extreme their allegations and supposed memories, the more they would be paid. Even their children joined in (they were paid in chocolate and other proletarian tooth-rot), and were induced to allege that they always used to cross the road whenever they passed my house, because they sensed that there was something wrong with – or rather, *in* – it. And who can argue with the intuitive wisdom of a child?

What discernment, what extraordinary foresight, the whole neighbourhood displayed – strictly in retrospect, of course. Looking back on it, everyone had known from the day I moved into number 17 that something strange was going on there. The house was too often in shadow, the curtains too often drawn, for all to have been well. But the whole neighbourhood was also too dim, and too blinded by the hope of gain, to realise that this vaunted intuition of theirs turned them into my accomplices, morally if not legally. For they had never voiced their misgivings, not once in all those years.

But how eagerly they informed upon me, once it was safe to do so! I don't suppose there was a house in the neighbourhood (except mine) which did not contain a stolen video or microwave oven: my neighbours were all happy enough to receive stolen goods, providing it was at the right price. They couldn't hang their washing out in their back gardens for fear of theft by their neighbours, and burglaries were as frequent as visits by the postman. Because of their dishonesty they hated and feared the police, whom they regarded as their oppressors. But as soon as they were on the right side of the law (for once in their lives), and as soon as they were convinced that the police were not in the slightest interested in the criminally-acquired goods in their homes, they sang like birds, making it all up as they went along but almost coming to believe their inventions to be the truth.

Yes, ladies and gentleman, Man is a born informer – or perhaps I should say *misinformer*. He loves to land his neighbours deep in trouble, even if he has to tell the most outrageous and transparent lies in order to do so, and even if his own conscience is not at all clear even before he bears false witness (I suppose it is necessary, in these times of mass ignorance, to point out that I allude here to one of the Ten Commandments, the ninth of them to be exact). Man, natural slave that he is, likes nothing more than to tell tales to the very authorities which he has previously affected to despise. If there is one characteristic which distinguishes Man from the lower animals (lower, that is, in intellectual, not moral, terms) it is not his speech, his erect gait, his ability to oppose his thumb and forefinger, his supposed rationality or his use of tools, but his secret burning desire to act the secret policeman.

So the world was treated for a time to the gratifying spectacle of the moral outrage of people who beat their wives regularly, neglected their children, not only coveted but actually stole their neighbour's goods, drank to excess, cheated the Social Security, shoplifted and were proud of it, refused as a matter of the highest principle to work and in general behaved without the slightest regard for the welfare or interests of others. And the reporters behaved towards them – admittedly not sincerely, but with their eye firmly fixed as always on the main chance – as if they were all Daniels come to judgment (as Antonio exclaims of Portia in *The Merchant of Venice*, Act 4, scene 1, a flawed masterpiece in my opinion, since Shylock is clearly the wronged party

44

in the play, and deserves exoneration rather than castigation).

I feel that I am beginning to digress again: I was speaking of the excessive interest in my case and what it signified.

Now I take it that a rational and moral man interests himself in subjects according to their intrinsic importance. To immerse oneself in trivialities is not only an intellectual, but a moral, weakness. So what transcendent importance did my case possess that it should have driven from the minds of men all other subjects of public concern for several weeks, indeed months?

The answer is, none.

Let me briefly remind you of the kind of world in which we have the honour to live. By the time you finish reading this page, ten children will have died throughout the world of diseases which are easily prevented or cheaply treated. By the time you finish reading all that I have to say, a thousand children will have died in this fashion – while you, with your tender so-called conscience, will have munched distractedly on more calories and other nutrients in the form of peanuts or chocolate – for who can sit long these days without eating? – than these children would have consumed in a week (had they survived). The total cost of saving these lives would have been negligible: less by far than that of your video machine, for example. But when you bought that video, did you give so much as a moment's thought to the thousand lives which might have been saved had you spent the money differently? A visit to any store which sells such goods would settle the question beyond doubt: it is interest-free credit which animates the soul of modern man, not the fate of the world's children.

Ignorance of these facts is something which you cannot plead, not unless you are blind and deaf and mentally retarded into the bargain. Information about the state of the world is literally inescapable nowadays. If you don't know about the latest epidemic in South America, the latest famine in Africa, the latest earthquake in Central Asia, or the latest civil war anywhere in the world, it is because you choose to remain in ignorance. And whether you like it or not, if you have done less than was within your power to save the lives of all the people who died in any of the above ways, you are as responsible for their deaths as if you had plunged an obsidian knife into their chests and torn out their still palpitating hearts (I quote, admittedly from memory, from Prescott's *The Conquest of Mexico*).

This is the latest and irrefutable conclusion of philosophy: that there is no moral difference between an act and an omission where the deleterious results of the act or omission are entirely predictable. It makes murderers of you all, ladies and gentlemen – and on an industrial scale, one might almost say.

No doubt my unwanted and unwonted disruption of your complacency has caused you by now to throw my book at the wall, figuratively if not quite literally. You are angry, with that thoroughly enjoyable anger to which the self-righteous are so priggishly prone. Preposterous, you exclaim, that this man should accuse us of being no better than he, and possibly even worse! Is it we, after all, who have been found guilty on fifteen counts of murder without extenuating circumstances?

Legally, I grant you, there may be a difference between us; but morally speaking (the plane on which I am moving in this short work), the difference between us is not at all to your advantage. For what is law but the institutionalised hypocrisy of society, backed by force?

Let us once again examine matters a little more closely. The distinction between us upon which you preen yourselves is that, while I killed by acts of commission, you killed and kill merely by acts of omission. You imagine this difference to be one of vital moral significance; but as I have said, not only I, but all modern philosophers of note dispute and refute this.

Doctors, for example, have long allowed their patients to die of pneumonia when, if they were to recover after treatment, they would lead a life only of suffering and further misery; and such doctors have been applauded for their humanity and wisdom. Yet those same doctors throw up their hands in horror at the very thought of actively intervening to procure the death of their patients, their happy release from useless suffering, by the injection of potassium for example. They cite the very same sanctity of life as the cause of their horror at the very idea of killing which they had entirely forgotten in the case of the old hemiplegic or dement whom they let die of pneumonia. It isn't life, therefore, which is sacrosanct, but life which partakes of certain qualities, the lack of which renders such life at best meaningless, at worst harmful to self and others.

This is a truth admitted by anyone of any philosophical or moral sensibility at all.

Well then, the doctor who does not leave to chance the release of his patients (and their relatives) from unbearable suffering, but who intervenes directly, not only decreases the sum of suffering in the world but increases the sum of justice. For can it be just that one person should suffer years of pain and misery because of a certain incurable medical condition, while another person with exactly the same medical condition escapes that suffering merely because he happens to contract pneumonia in the course of it – and all of this when the remedy lies close at hand, but is unused merely because of a certain hypocritical and self-regarding fastidiousness on the part of the doctor?

The doctor who actively performs euthanasia is thus the moral superior of one who leaves his patients to die at nature's cruel whim, and the latter is in grave error (no pun intended, it would be out of place) if he imagines that his unwillingness to apply the *coup de grace* is a point in his favour. On the contrary, he is a coward, nothing more.

By now it must be clear, even to the least intellectually alert among you, where my argument is leading. I am your moral superior because, like the doctor who practises active euthanasia, I do not do my killing at random: I choose who is to die by my own hand, according to rational and humane criteria. By contrast, your acts of omission, which are responsible for vastly greater numbers of deaths than the numbers which I have ever aspired to bring about, strike the just and the unjust alike: you kill like the madman who enters a supermarket and mows down the customers until he is overpowered or himself shot dead.

But, you will object, happy at last to have found an argument to refute one of mine, you are just as guilty as we of the acts of omission with which you reproach us, in addition to which you have actively ended the lives of fifteen others (or twenty-two, depending on how you look at it). Therefore, having been responsible for more deaths than we, you still deserve the condemnation and punishment to which you have been subjected.

I like a good discussion and, as the psychiatrists said, for once not missing their mark (they say so much that, by the laws of chance, some of what they say must be true), I like to win. Easy victories, however, do not greatly please or interest me. It is the intellectual contest which appeals to me. Therefore, while I applaud your attempt to refute me, honesty compels me to protest at the extreme feebleness of your argument, which partakes of empirical and logical error in equal measure.

But let us suppose for the moment that a part of what you say is accurate: that in addition to having caused as many deaths as you by acts of omission, I have caused fifteen (or twenty-two) deaths by acts of commission.

Does this prove that I deserve to be imprisoned for the rest of my life and never released?

Not at all. For the fact is that our mutual acts of omission – the mutuality of which is merely momentarily hypothesised, be it remembered – have caused so many deaths, adding up to thousands if not tens of thousands over a lifetime, that the addition of a mere fifteen (no, let me put your argument at its strongest, let me say the addition of a mere twenty-two) deaths cannot weigh significantly in the balance. For if I were to ask you which man was worse, the man who was responsible in his lifetime for the deaths of 10,739 people, or the one who was responsible for 10,761, you would look at me in puzzlement and no doubt conclude that anyone who could ask such a question was himself morally perverse. It is obvious, you would say when you had recovered from the strangeness of the question, that there is and can be nothing to choose between them, and that, on the contrary, to make such pettifogging distinctions is psychologically to condone at least one of the perpetrators ('At least,' the former will be able to say of the latter, 'I am not as bad as he'), and to miss entirely the monstrousness of the situation as a whole. Was Auschwitz worse – morally worse, I mean, not empirically worse – than Treblinka?

But in any case, I do not even grant you the initial premise of your argument, that your and my acts of omission were in any way comparable. You who read this are likely to be much more comfortably placed than ever I was: and thus to allay the hunger of the starving millions and to cure the equally large numbers of sick of their eminently curable diseases was much more within your power than it ever was within mine. For how much did I ever earn as a minor functionary of local government, denied promotion by a combination of prejudice against my small stature and suburban whine, and a typically bureaucratic dislike of my habits of independent thought, my refusal to toe the line and my devastatingly ironical criticism of the semi-literate circulars which descended on us regularly from on high? I earned a mere pittance, nothing more.

I see a sneer spread over your face. You, who have at your disposal larger sums of money for luxuries than I ever had for necessities! (In general, and from the literary point of view, I despise exclamation marks, but I think the preceding sentence merits one.) In short, you accuse me of special pleading, though nothing could be further from the truth.

I never received more than a thousand pounds a month for my work at the Housing Department, and often less. Of this, I spent a third on food and electricity, a further third on the repayment of my mortgage, and rather more than an eighth on the maintenance of my car, the cheapest possible vehicle which actually ran. This left me with less than two hundred pounds a month for everything else: clothes, holidays, entertainment, furnishings and saving for my old age. Not exactly a life of opulence, I think you are forced to admit.

On what could I have economised to make charitable donations? I did not eat extravagantly, though I admit that a balanced vegan diet involves expenditure not incurred by those who consume less ethical diets. I had to consider the welfare of factory farm animals, however, and as I have already mentioned, I am not a man who is prepared to compromise on principles.

But did you really need a car, you ask? Your question demonstrates that you have never been dependent on public transport for your mobility. In this society, arranged as it is purely for the convenience of the rich, a person without a car is nothing, indeed is regarded with suspicion, almost as a criminal. Not to own a car is taken as a moral failing, rather like a lack of cleanliness or drunkenness. Oh yes, I *could* have lived (I suppose) without a car, if I had been resigned to count my house as a prison, never to go out at times convenient to myself, slowly to develop the agoraphobia which afflicted so many of the housewives around me. For agoraphobia starts as a habit and ends up as a disease.

Well then, you continue, there was always your mortgage. Did a man in your position have to buy his own house, rather than rent one? Yes, more than any other kind of man, in fact. There was no one from whom I should eventually have inherited a house or its equivalent in ready money: on the contrary, I shall inherit from my mother only the expenses of her funeral. To throw oneself on the mercy of the Housing Department (as I am in a position to know better than anyone) is like seeking comfort in a torture chamber, besides which the Department disposes of no accommodation of a standard appropriate to the needs of one such as I. As for private landlords, they are all bloodsuckers, preying unmercifully on the unfortunates who have no place to call their own.

No, ladies and gentlemen, my mortgage was not so much an extravagance, as an elementary form of self-defence, a sheer necessity.

Whichever way you look at it, I had little money to spare, unlike those of you with your Persian carpets, works of art and other luxurious baubles and gewgaws. It is you – the heartless rich – who should be locked up as mass murderers, not me (I pondered here long and hard over whether to write *I* or *me*, and decided finally on *me* because it gives a more natural and spontaneous effect, though I know *I* to be grammatically correct. I do not wish, however, to be dismissed as a mere pedantic autodidact). If I had been paid what I was worth by the Department, or even half of what I was worth, instead of the gross overpayment of footballers who can hardly string sufficient words together to form a coherent sentence, or of philistine businessmen whose creed is greed, perhaps matters would have been different, and I might have been as guilty as you of murderous acts of omission: as it was, however, it was you, not I, who were (and still are) guilty of them. And in apportioning moral responsibility, it is necessary to stick to the facts, not promiscuously to invent mere might-have-beens.

The inescapable conclusion, then, is that you have more blood on your hands than I. Your righteous indignation stands revealed as a bluff. No amount of protestation on your part will wash off the blood: your hands are more indelibly bloodstained than Lady Macbeth's (*Macbeth*, Act 5, scene 1).

And I haven't finished my indictment of your selective morality yet, not by a long way. Consider for a moment the numbers of people who are killed and tortured every day around the world in wars and by oppressive or repressive regimes. But what has this to do with either us or the matter in hand, you exclaim, and why do you bring it up now? Aren't you just trying to divert our attention from the horrible crimes you yourself committed?

On the contrary, I am only trying to be morally consistent, for without consistency there can be no morality. And ever since Socrates, the best method of achieving consistency has been to unmask its opposite.

The question, therefore, which I now want to ask you is the following: From where do you suppose that the armaments to pursue these wars and to uphold these oppressive and repressive regimes originate? And the answer, of course, is from the country in which you happen to live (among others, admittedly), and whose authorities have seen fit to pass judgment on me.

We can't help that, you say. We are not arms salesmen; we are not involved in the manufacture of armaments; we are insurance salesmen, car dealers, gastroenterologists, or whatever else it may be. We have nothing to do with the arms trade.

Oh but you do, ladies and gentlemen, you do, whether you acknowledge it or not. Every time you purchase or use foreign goods (and that is every day of the week), you benefit from precisely that trade: for were it not for the export of arms, our balance of payments would be worse than it already is. And this in turn would mean that our currency would depreciate, perhaps to such an extent that the foreign goods to which you have become so accustomed would be placed beyond your financial reach. So rather than go without your German car, your French cheese and wine, your Greek yoghurt, your Italian salami and your Japanese cameras and video, you close your eyes to the evident fact that their purchase is possible only through sales of arms to despots who slaughter the peasants of the world and bring about famines to further their own ends. By insisting on your foreign luxuries, you make the torture chambers safe for autocracy. So once again, you are an accessory to murder: moreover, murder on a vast scale. And an accessory to murder is, morally speaking, a murderer.

You retort, naturally enough (for there is no one angrier than the justly-accused), that I go too far with my argument. For once again you accuse me of living in the same society as you, and therefore of having benefitted to the same extent as you from the arms trade. Besides which, you add, a man who lives in a society of many millions can hardly be deemed responsible for everything which goes on within it, or is done in its name by its government. There is no responsibility without power.

I grant a certain superficial plausibility to your arguments, ladies and gentlemen, though these arguments are meretricious rather than meritorious. On closer analysis, of course, they dissolve like morning mist in the sunlight, and vanish without trace. For I am not claiming that you are solely or even largely responsible for your country's wholehearted participation in the iniquitous trade; but you are responsible to the extent that you benefit from it and do nothing to stop it. I claim only that you share in the general blame, which being incalculably vast, leaves each individual so great a portion that he cannot point the finger at me with any moral authority whatever – even if my activities were reprehensible, which I deny and shall in due course prove.

I do not wish to boast, or make myself out to be better than I am, but I think I may fairly claim to have done all that was within my limited power to bring a halt to this commercialised iniquity, the arms trade. I have written on innumerable occasions to Members of Parliament and government ministers, to protest against some particularly egregious (but profitable) contract to supply arms to foreign despots. Only two weeks before my arrest, in fact, I wrote to the Minister of Overseas Development to declare my total opposition to, repudiation of and disgust with the sale of twenty-six jet trainers to the government of the Republic of Ngombia. I cannot do better, I think, than to reproduce my letter:

Dear Mr Jones,

I am writing to you once again to draw your attention to agreement to supply twenty-six jet trainers to the repressive military government of the Republic of Ngombia.

As you know, the government of that country has been engaged now for more than a decade upon a war of extermination against the aboriginal peoples who inhabit the country's remaining rain forests.

The government of Ngombia states that the jets will be used for training purposes only. Lies! They are all too easily adapted for dropping napalm, cluster, anti-personnel and phosphorus bombs, and also for the mounting of rockets, as you very well know.

In any case, for what purpose does Ngombia need trained pilots, if not for these activities? She has no external enemies from whom she needs to defend herself.

The guarantees given by the government of Ngombia

with regard to the so-call pacific use of the trainers are therefore not worth the paper they are written on. On three separate occasions that government has broken a ceasefire with the rebels.

There is only one possible conclusion: that an export licence for the jets has been granted to serve the interests a) of arms manufacturers and dealers and b) of the international logging companies, on whose behalf the genocide of the aboriginals is being committed. Moreover, the savage destruction of the rainforests puts the ecological balance of the entire planet at risk, will damage the ozone layer beyond repair, and lead to an exponential increase in the rate of fatal skin cancer.

Those who fail to oppose this cynical sale of sophisticated weaponry to a brutal and repressive government, or even worse support it, are guilty beyond all question of a) murder by skin cancer and b) genocide against innocent and harmless people. They will have committed crimes against humanity.

Yours in indignation,
Graham Underwood

A powerful letter, I flatter myself.

And what did I receive in return? The following, not written by the great man himself, oh dear no, he is far too busy to attend to mere constituents like me, but by someone (a young sprig from Oxford, no doubt, with political ambitions of his own) calling himself Jones's parliamentary private secretary:

Dear Mr Underwood,

I have been asked by the Minister, the Rt Hon. Mr Sopwith Jones MP, to reply on his behalf to your letter of the 7th ult. He asks me to make the following points:

i) There is no evidence of genocidal intent by the Government of Ngombia, with whom Her Majesty's Government enjoys excellent political, economic and diplomatic relations.

ii) The competition in the field of supply of jet trainers is fierce, and if we had not agreed to supply them, then one of our competitors most certainly would have done so.

iii) The order represents a considerable boost to our exports and therefore to our balance of payments, and secures thousands of jobs for the foreseeable future at a time of high unemployment.

> Yours sincerely,
> Herbert Robinson
> Parliamentary Private Secretary
> to the Rt Hon Mr Sopwith Jones MP

Not even an apology for the delay in replying! (I think a further exclamation mark is more than justified in the circumstances.) And what weasel words, immaculately typed on thick-woven cream-coloured paper with an embossed green crest, all paid for by the taxpayer, I need hardly add.

If we don't sell them, someone else will: what kind of argument is that, from the moral point of view? Does it excuse *Topf und Sohn*, the suppliers of gas ovens to the SS? Can a burglar argue that if it hadn't been he, someone else would have burgled the house, because burglary is so common these days? What would Mr Sopwith Jones have replied if I had argued successfully in court that had I not killed my 'victims', they would have died of a heart attack or of cancer anyway?

Of course, it is well-known that Mr Sopwith Jones would support government policy to the portals of Hell and beyond, if he thought it would preserve his seat in Parliament at the next election. As for the so-called opposition in our so-called democracy, it speaks vociferously of morality while it is out of office, but as soon as it is elected to office it becomes just as amoral as the outgoing government. And this, ladies and gentlemen, is the calibre of the men who make decisions affecting the lives and deaths of millions of people, supposedly on our behalf.

Writing to my Member of Parliament was not the only

method by which I tried (unsuccessfully, it is true, but the virtue is in the effort) to bring about an end to this merchandising of the means of mass death. When our local council declared the borough a nuclear-free zone (a small step, but one in the right direction), I organised a meeting in the Housing Department to pressure the council to declare the borough an arms industry-free zone as well. My superior in the department tried to reprimand me for having arranged the meeting during working hours: but I fought him all the way, rulebook in hand. It was a blatant attempt, I said, to suppress freedom of speech and association: and I pointed out that under our terms and conditions of service, staff had the right to hold a reasonable number of meetings which directly affected their interests. And what could have been of greater interest to them than the moral climate of the borough in which, and for which, they worked? My superior deeply resented my victory over him, and has (or rather had) been seeking revenge ever since; but I have (or had) been too clever for him. He never succeeded in his aim of having me dismissed.

The motion at the meeting was passed by an overwhelming majority, but the council did nothing, arguing that there were no arms factories in the borough in any case. But when I wrote to the leader of the council to point out that there were no nuclear installations in the borough either, but that that had not deterred the council from declaring the borough a nuclear-free zone, he wrote back to tell me (not in so many words, of course) that it was none of my business: none of my business, I being merely a citizen and elector!

I wrote to the newspapers as well. In all, I had seven letters published, of a total of one hundred and eighty-six written. And it is pretended that the press is free in this country! Of the seven which were published, six were in the local newspapers, and only one in a national, though the ratio of letters addressed to each was precisely the reverse. Whether you agree with my views or not, I think I have demonstrated sufficiently that I can argue cogently and coherently. The failure of the national newspapers to publish my letters therefore puzzled me at first, especially when I compared what I had written with what was published in the correspondence columns, which was frequently trivial and inconsequential. But then I realised that letters were published not according to merit or the intrinsic interest of their contents, but according to who the editor supposed the correspondent was. And this he guessed by the address from which the letters were sent: unless, of course, the correspondent happened to be a public figure of note, in which case publication was automatic, without reference to the address.

I had to be satisfied with occasional successes in the *Eastham Evening Telegraph* (incorporating the *Evening Messenger*) and latterly with the *Eastham Free Press*, one of those weekly newspapers consisting mainly of small ads which is pushed through your letterbox whether you want it or not. The correspondence columns of such publications, indeed the publications in their entirety, are of course more concerned with trivial local matters than with the great issues of the day, but one has regrettably to start somewhere. No one with an important message is heard straight away. (The strongest man in the world is the man who stands most alone: Ibsen, *An Enemy of the People*.)

I could, of course, give you further examples. It is not by guns alone that Man kills his fellow Man. For it is beyond question that the smoking of cigarettes is now the greatest cause of preventable death among adults in the world. And it should come as no surprise to you that some of the largest tobacco companies in the world are owned, and have their headquarters, in your own capital city.

And what of it, you ask? What has this to do with us?

Well, ladies and gentlemen, cigarette sales have been falling in countries where the harmful effects of smoking have been widely publicised (no thanks to the companies, of course, quite the reverse). And what do you suppose the tobacco companies have done to protect their profits, to maintain the flow of dividends not only to the pockets of individual shareholders but to the institutional buyers of their shares? They have tried to increase their sales of cigarettes in countries where the authorities are too weak and poor to resist their bribes, and where the people are pathetically susceptible to anything which gives them the impression they are partaking of the rich lifestyle of Europe and America.

Still you don't see, of course, what any of this has to do with you. You remind me of Pilate, who refused to make a choice as to which of the Palestinian prisoners should be released, on the grounds that it was none of his business.

But answer me this: who are the shareholders in the tobacco companies? Before you point the finger at others, I will answer for you: you are the shareholders. But we have no share certificates, you protest; we receive no dividends. Not directly, I grant you; but all of you have pension funds, or contribute to pension schemes, and – as is well-known – they are the largest investors by far in the stock market. And such is the size and profitability of the tobacco companies that no pension fund could afford to be without a block of shares in them.

Perhaps you feel a little less smug after my demonstration, but the really important question relates not to your feelings but to your deeds. Now that you know beyond doubt that you are investing in Third World lung cancer, bronchitis and heart disease, what are you going to do about it? Are you willing to forgo the security of your old age so that the poor will not die of the diseases of the rich? Will you demand of your pension fund managers that they divest the fund of shares whose value increases in proportion to the numbers of deaths caused?

It isn't only the tobacco companies of which I speak, however: it is the whole iniquitous system by which pharmaceutical companies, for example, profit from suffering, and export to other countries drugs which are deemed too dangerous for sale in their home country; and food companies which deliberately create a taste for their expensive junk products of no nutritional value in countries in which the people do not have money enough to feed themselves properly. Neither are the oil companies to be excluded, which are destroying the remaining wildernesses of the world, only that you may travel cheaply (but meaninglessly) between A and B, in the process destroying not only whole peoples and cultures, but entire species of animals and plants. Species, in fact, are dying out at the rate of one a day.

If shares in all the death-dealing companies and industries were excluded from the portfolios of the pension funds, nothing would remain; but I do not think I should be wrong in assuming that you have done nothing to protest against this global iniquity, your security being more important to you than the survival of the planet and its biosphere. I, on the other hand, bought a single share in many such companies to embarrass their chairmen at the annual general meeting by asking difficult questions. Their anger in reply was more than sufficient proof of their guilt.

Thus, I think you will concede that I have done all within my unfortunately limited power to bring about the end of our country's complicity in indiscriminate slaughter. I ask you now to look into your own hearts and ask whether you can say as much for yourselves: you with your connections to the powerful, with your money and your leisure. And if the answer is no, which of us is the truly guilty party?

I have mentioned already my disdain for psychiatrists, a mongrel breed if ever there was one, claiming to be scientists and yet humanists at the same time, when in reality they are officially-licensed and highly-paid gossips. But one among them once wrote something true and important (though naturally he was despised for it by his professional colleagues, who conspired to ruin his career by withdrawing his right to practise). I refer to R.D.Laing, who wrote:

> We are all murderers and prostitutes – no matter to what culture, society, class, nation one belongs, no matter how normal, moral or mature one takes oneself to be.

The unvarnished truth, ladies and gentlemen, whether you like it or not. But at least I have tried, consistently and without fail, to escape this condition. Are you able to say the same? And if not, should we not be changing places?

6

But still I feel that I have not quite said what I set out to say (your objections having obstructed the flow of my argument). I intended to answer definitively the question of why my case should have aroused so much interest around the world. First, of course, I had to establish beyond dispute the statistical insignificance of what I did, compared with so many other acts and omissions of the Twentieth Century. For without such a clear demonstration, my puzzlement at my own notoriety might have seemed strange and even pathological to you, brought up as you are in a consumer society not to look behind appearances. No, for you as for the great majority of Mankind, all that glisters really is gold; and, by a logically faulty process of reasoning, you and it (the majority) believe the reverse to be the case also, namely that all that fails to glister is dross of no value. This law, if I may call it such, holds sway in every sphere, but particularly in the moral. You expect your heroes and your villains to be visibly and obviously such; many times I have caught people peering hard into my face as if expecting to perceive there the mark of Cain (*Genesis*, Chapter 4, verse 15).

Second, in proving that you are responsible for many more deaths than I, I have uncovered a likely motive for your obsessive interest in my case: a desire to conceal your own guilt by projecting it (as the Freudians put it in their obscurantist language) on to me.

But even this, I venture to suggest, does not adequately

explain why nine authors to my certain knowledge (which may, in this instance, be incomplete) have been commissioned by publishers to write books about me and my life, which until now has been one of the utmost obscurity, of no particular interest even to myself. Publishers, after all, are not philanthropists, and would not have signed such contracts unless they thought it were profitable to have done so; and need I point out that publishers' profits derive from sales of their books to the public? A film company is also said to be interested in my story.

No, ladies and gentlemen, in answering the question as to why my activities have been and are of such great interest to so many, we are inevitably dealing with human psychology's equivalent of the dark side of the moon, not with matters which are so transparent that they require no analysis or elucidation.

Let me first point out that I am by no means what is known as a common murderer. This is not to say that one can learn nothing by the study of the latter: and indeed, since the public has insisted upon subsuming me under that category, but writ very much larger, and since it is the mentality of the public which we are now investigating, a few observations on common murderers may not be entirely out of place.

You will not be surprised to hear that I have now met many of this species in my peregrinations through the English *gulag*. They each of them spend their first few days of incarceration in the prison hospital, as if murder were an illness and not a natural act which has survived all attempts down the ages to suppress it, and which must therefore be considered a perfectly normal and universal part of human behaviour. (And should what is normal, I ask, be liable to punishment?) The reason murderers are treated thus on their arrival in prison, however, is that they are thought to be susceptible to suicide, an event which would cause the prison authorities much embarrassment, thanks to the eternal vigilance of our press, which is constantly on the alert for any opportunity to make pointless trouble and thus increase circulation, though the suicide of a murderer would save the taxpayer much expense in the long (and even the short) run. And if there's one thing the warders hate more than a live prisoner, it's a dead one: not because of any humanitarian sentiment, of which they are entirely innocent, but because of all the forms they have to fill in after a prisoner's death. (Most of the warders, I have observed, stick their tongues out with the effort of writing longhand.)

On his arrival in prison, therefore, a murderer (or *suspected* murderer, according to the hypocritical pretence that a man is innocent until proven guilty) is stripped even of normal prison clothes and dressed in shorts and a T-shirt of tough and shiny man-made fibre, the colour of loose faeces. He is placed in a cell completely devoid of furniture or other possible appurtenances of suicide. And there he is left to rot for a few days until, despairing of the alternative, he agrees to go on living.

This ritual, carried out in the name of humanity – that is to say, the welfare of the murderer – has for its true purpose the establishment of who is to be master, that's all. In prison, a man is not the possessor of his own life: which is another reason why the warders hate a suicide: as far as they are concerned, it is a kind of robbery.

How sordid, uncomplicated and lacking in philosophical content are the motives of the common murderer, even when, purely for form's sake, he denies his guilt! It is absurd and grossly unjust to place me in the same category. On the very day I was arrested and taken to prison, for example, a doctor accused of murdering his wife was among my fellow-inductees into the institution, or 'freshmen of the University of Crime', as one screw jocularly put it, imagining he was being both witty and erudite.

The doctor's wife had died of an injection into the veins of her right arm. From the fact that, during life, she was right-handed, even our less-than-intellectually-gifted constabulary was able to deduce that something suspicious had occurred. And with a doctor in the house, the search for a suspect was not a prolonged one.

I grew intimate with the doctor, who until his arrest had been the epitome of complacent and snobbish prosperity. He was glad of the opportunity to talk to someone of intelligence and culture once his period of solitary confinement was over, but he was a perfect monster of egotism, precisely as I would have expected of a man of his class and social standing who had fallen on hard times. He talked only of himself, and evinced no interest in either me or my case. He told me that the police were absurd, incompetent, unable to detect the most obvious contradictions in their so-called evidence against him, that his lawyer had told him that after his release, which would happen at the latest within two weeks, there being no case to answer, he would file suit for wrongful arrest and imprisonment, since anyone should have realised that there could not possibly have been a motive for him to kill his wife – especially when he had so much to lose by doing so, since he was the local representative of the British Medical Association, among other important positions.

This doctor, this scion of the so-called self-regulating and ethical profession of medicine, also informed me that his wife had just discovered that he was having an affair with his receptionist, twenty years his junior. She threatened him at once with divorce proceedings, unless he immediately and unconditionally cease all contact with the receptionist, in short sacked her and promised never even to think of her again. The silly fool thought he was in love with her, and even worse, that she was in love with him: so he told his wife that though he loved her still, it was in a different way from the way in which he loved the receptionist. There never was a clearer case of wanting your cake and eating it.

His wife, of course, would have none of it, and sued for divorce. Because of the divorce laws, he faced the prospect not only of parting with half his possessions, but of supporting her with much of his income for the rest of his days. This was more than he could bear: his house, he told me, was an Elizabethan manor, with three acres of gardens, and it was not difficult to guess what exchanging it for an ordinary dwelling (still a hundred times better and more comfortable than mine) would have meant to him. Priding himself on his technical knowledge of poisons, by means of which he thought to evade the law, he killed her, though he was so naive and lacking in elementary technique (or perhaps so overexcited by his task), that he could scarcely have made his guilt plainer than if he had phoned the police himself and confessed on the spot.

Here, symbolically, you see represented the injustice of our society. I possessed no university diploma, nor even school certificate, and was therefore never able to raise myself above the level of humble clerk: whenever I applied for something better, the first question was, Where are your qualifications? My natural abilities counted for nothing. Whereas this man, this doctor, who had jumped a hundred scholastic hurdles and who could have used his diplomas as wallpaper if he had had a mind to do so, lived in a luxury of which it would have been pointless even for me to dream. Yet he was caught at once, within twenty-four hours, whereas I was caught only after twenty-four years (to round up the figure slightly for rhetorical effect), after twenty-two cases, seven of which still remain to be elucidated and perhaps never will be; and caught, moreover, only by the unluckiest of chances. Which of us, I ask you, ladies and gentlemen, displayed the more native talent, the more intelligence, and which of us, in a genuine meritocracy, would have risen higher in the social scale? But of course, we do not live in a meritocracy.

Now it is true that the doctor went through a suicidal stage, like all the other common murderers of my acquaintance. The naive among you – that is to say, the vast majority – might suppose that this stage had something to do with remorse, and all that Raskolnikov kind of crap. (Here, I believe, I have artfully combined two disparate literary references and melded them into a convincing whole: J.D.Salinger's *The Catcher in the Rye* and Dostoyevsky's *Crime and Punishment*. Without wishing to appear boastful, I ask you whether you think that a man of ordinary capacities could have combined such references in this fashion? Is it not socially wasteful that such a man should be condemned to languish in prison, and likewise that he was formerly condemned to languish in the lower reaches of a local government bureaucracy? Such, ladies and gentlemen, is the society in which we live.) No, it is not remorse that leads a man like the medical uxoricide to consider death: his own, this time. It is sorrow and bitterness at the realisation of all he has lost, and will never have again: wealth, social position and so forth. He is in mourning for his life – this time I adapt from Chekhov, ironically in this context. My adaptation is from the answer Masha gives in *The Seagull*, Act 1, to Medvedenko's question as to why she always wears black.

The suicidal phase soon passes, unless there is a special reason why it should not: and then it becomes the pseudosuicidal phase. The purpose of this phase is to keep the murderer in the prison hospital as long as possible, because it is more comfortable there than in the rest of the prison. There is a snooker table, and the television is on all the time: home from home for most people, in fact. And some prisoners use the hospital as a refuge from other prisoners. I knew a young man accused of a murderer of which he was genuinely innocent (though he wasn't innocent *tout court*, of course – I should perhaps explain that I am not opposed to the use of foreign phrases when they are used not as a display of erudition but to express something for which there is no equivalent in English). The young man had lived all his life in a criminal environment and was a small-time recipient of stolen goods (the only work which he had ever done), for which he had already served several short sentences. One day he took delivery of a consignment from his usual suppliers of stolen goods, wrapped in a thick plastic bag which they asked him to look after for a while, until they came to fetch it again. Then the police arrived: the consignment was a body and he had been well and truly set up. The young man knew with whom he was dealing: that is to say, he knew better than to tell the police the truth about the body, for the killers would not have hesitated to kill again, using the same method of disposal. It was safer for him to admit to the crime which he never committed.

Unfortunately for him, the murdered man had belonged to a gang which was the rival of that which killed him. One of its members was already in the prison, and was under the impression that the young man accused of the murder was a full participant in the killing of his colleague. A severe beating was easily arranged: but a revenge killing would take a little longer to organise, though it was inevitable sooner or later. A dunking in the boiling vats in the prison kitchens, where many prisoners worked, or a slash in the throat with a razor made from prison materials, or even a hanging: all could be arranged in the long run. The young man lived in fear, starting at his own shadow, though he was relatively safe in the hospital wing.

But only relatively, mind you: a hit man could easily enough fake his way into the hospital, bluffing his way past the doctor whose only interest in whether his patients lived or died was bureaucratic (it was more trouble if they died), and kill him there. Hence he greeted each new arrival in the hospital with apprehension: was this to be his executioner? And he knew that he would have to live in fear all the rest of his days. Criminals, ladies and gentlemen, are just like you: they have short memories for the harm they do, but long ones for the harm which they imagine has been done to them.

Nevertheless, the hospital wing was the young man's best chance of survival in the circumstances, and every time it was suggested that he should leave it, he scratched his wrists with any piece of metal which came to hand, as a warning to the screws that he would kill himself if he were moved. Brutal but nonetheless sticklers for bureaucratic form, the screws never dared call his bluff: they were terrified of the Chief Inspector of Prisons, a retired woman judge who dressed in tweeds and smoked a cheroot, who thought that the prisons should be run like Montessori schools, and who fulminated in public every time a prisoner succeeded in killing himself. She called for a public enquiry whenever this happened, instead of calling for research into how this laudable and highly economical activity might be increased among the involuntary guests of the government.

Like most bullies, however, the screws were also cowards: the very name of the retired judge struck terror into their hearts, and they could only say what they really thought of her when they had drunk (or *sunk*, as they put it so elegantly among themselves) several pints of beer – that is to say, every night.

This is the atmosphere in which I, who could and should have been an artist, and would have been had there been any justice in the world, am obliged to live.

Now the whole point of my story about the young man is that the behaviour of the man falsely accused of murder, but unable to defend himself, and that of the real (common) murderer, is in every way identical and indistinguishable. And the screws, not without reason, treated them exactly the same.

And this, ladies and gentlemen, is another irrefutable proof, if a further one is needed, of my assertion that, when it comes to murder, guilt and innocence represent a distinction without a difference: an error rightly condemned by all philosophers.

7

Not being a professional writer, I have begun to lose my thread again. If I had been born in the right circumstances, perhaps I might have contributed to literature: for I flatter myself that I possess some natural talent in that direction, and only the overwhelmingly urgent need to earn a living prevented me from doing so.

Besides, conditions in prison are hardly conducive to the creation of works of literary perfection. Whoever designed prisons knew that a vital component of Hell was continual noise, so he built them of materials that not only transmitted the faintest sound, but amplified it by a hundred times. Outside its walls, we are told, not a sparrow falls but our Heavenly Father takes cognizance of the fact (Matthew, Chapter 11, verse 29); inside its walls, not a prisoner farts (to use the vernacular for a moment) but the building vibrates on the Richter scale. And when a real commotion breaks out – a whistle alarm, say – Armageddon (Revelation, Chapter 16, verse 16) would be like a Zen garden by comparison.

There was precisely such an alarm on my landing only ten minutes before I wrote this, for example. I am still trembling slightly. The cell of one of my neighbours, a common criminal, was searched by two screws for illicit radio parts (what is not permitted in prison is forbidden). They came across a blackish substance stuffed into the mattress, for which the prisoner made a grab in an attempt to swallow the evidence. Can you wonder that the law is so despised when it is punishable to possess a substance which it is not illegal actually to have taken? If I were trying to devise a system worthy of the contempt of every intelligent person, I could think of no better.

Anyway, the screws tried to stop the con (the coarsening of my language is a product of my environment, ladies and gentlemen) by force. He resisted and punched one of the screws. The other blew his whistle. Those who have never heard a prison whistle would not credit how loud a single blast of such a puny instrument can be, especially in a confined space: enough to make hear the dead who were deaf in life. This overture was swiftly followed by the symphonic sound of the boots of twenty screws on the Victorian ironwork stairs which lead to our landing. They came like children rushing for a treat. The next thing I heard was a scream of 'Fuck you, you pig!' – another three days' remission lost, on the charge 'That you did use insulting language to Officer Bryden while he was carrying out his lawful duties, namely that you did say "Fuck you, you fucking pig" to him.' (Prison officers, like policemen, are never content to confine themselves merely to the evidence.) Then came the sound of a man being subdued by having his arms twisted behind him, to a chorus of 'Don't move, keep still, you dumb shit!' And finally, the retreat of the screws, carrying the prisoner with them as he protested in a scream that they were breaking his arms, back down the ironwork stairs to the solitary confinement cells beneath: and all this taking place in the auditory equivalent of a hall of mirrors.

I ask you, ladies and gentlemen, how is a man – especially of my nervous disposition – supposed to develop an argument, and express it in an elegant prose style, when he is subject to such commotions which, moreover, can break out at any time of the day or night, and which, when they happen at night, leave him exhausted and anxious the next day for lack of sleep?

72

What could anyone have done to deserve such an experience as this?

But I started several pages ago to try to explain the excessive, and indeed unhealthy, public interest in my case, and now I shall disclose my explanation to you without further digression, in case another commotion breaks out on my landing and makes me lose my thread once more: *I have only done what you, in your heart of hearts, have always wanted to do.*

But of course you cannot acknowledge it, even to yourself, and therefore you transform me from hero to villain, a villain so villainous indeed that you pretend you cannot even understand me. This is what the Freudians call *reaction formation*, though of course I do not hold completely with their psychological system, which is burdened with a great deal of implausible elaboration.

Nor do I expect you to accept what I say without protest. Indeed, the very vehemence of your reaction demonstrates that I have touched a raw nerve with you. It is bad enough that I should have proved to your satisfaction that you are morally worse than I; but you find it intolerable that I should now go on to demonstrate that I have in any case only carried out in practice your innermost desires, upon which you were too cowardly to act yourself.

But many famous authors have recognised the truth of what I say, ladies and gentlemen. You will find in them a frank avowal of the most murderous desires, usually – but not always – in conjunction with sadistic fantasies, from which I have never suffered, at least not as an adult. On the contrary, I consider myself an idealist and a humanitarian.

I go to the authors, ladies and gentlemen, precisely because they have penetrated into the deepest recesses of the human mind, where others fear to think. They ruthlessly tear away the flimsy facades which you so easily erect to hide your true nature from others and

73

from yourselves. And I am modest enough to believe that I have something to learn from the sages of the past. They knew a thing or two.

Let us start with the Marquis de Sade, accused by some of being a tedious and even talentless writer: but this is surely the jealousy of those disappointed authors who are as likely to have an *ism* named after them as they are to sprout wings and ascend directly to heaven from somewhere in Jerusalem. I had to read him in a semi-clandestine fashion even now, two centuries later, so subversive of good order and discipline (as they call it in the prison) is he considered: I did not want the librarian to know what I was reading in case he would one day use this information to testify against me:

> We are going to describe crime [the Marquis means murder] as it is, that is to say always triumphant and sublime . . . while virtue is always wretched and sad.

Yes, the Marquis, despite being an aristocrat, hits here upon an essential truth: that Man is attracted to killing as a moth to the flame. Have you never wondered why in literature it is always the evil characters who have the best lines, the firmest delineation, and who remain forever fixed in the mind? Or why the Hell of Hieronymus Bosch should be so vivid, while all paintings of Paradise are so anaemic and passionless, leaving no trace in the mind? Take the Koran: what is its vision of Heaven? Of men lying about forever on golden couches in verdant gardens, being served cool refreshing drinks by virgin nymphomaniac maidens who never grow old, or tire of serving. One can see the attraction of this kind of Paradise to men who have spent their lives in the desert, around and about camels. But as a way of spending a week, let alone an eternity, it is a little restricted.

Man being what he is, eternal bliss simply cannot be imagined. Man is not only a problem-solving animal, but a problem-creating one. He cannot live without difficulties, and from time to time there are riots, even in Switzerland, whose perfection eventually enrages the inhabitants who have created it. He – that is, Man – cannot bear too much good order and happiness, any more than he can bear too much reality (T.S.Eliot, *Four Quartets*); no sooner does he arrive in a comfortable billet than he begins to look around for trouble. Bliss soon palls: ergo, it cannot exist. Merely to think about heaven soon induces a kind of stupor.

It is quite otherwise with hell, of course, and it is perfectly easy to imagine eternal torment. And when you put your mind to it, there are no end of perpetual punishments, gross or subtle, you can devise.

What does this prove, you ask? Nothing more – but also nothing less – than that Man has a natural vocation for all that is vicious, harmful and antisocial. To select some men for punishment is thus not only futile, but a mere exercise in scapegoating.

Let us return to the authors: though they are but straws in the wind of my argument. If de Sade had been the only example I could quote, if he were merely a sterile proof only of the extent and catholicism of my reading in the public library, well then, I might grant that it were possible to dismiss him as a mere aberration in the history of literature. But he is not the only one, or the greatest. Dostoyevsky, in *The Brothers Karamazov*, tells us that:

> In every man ... a demon lies hidden – the demon of rage, the demon of lustful heat at the screams of the tortured victim, the dream of lawlessness let off the chain.

No doubt you will wonder how it happened that a formally uneducated man such as I can quote these passages by heart in this extremely erudite fashion. The answer is simple: when I came across them in the public library I recognised at once that they not only conveyed an important truth, but they might be useful to me one day, and I branded them indelibly into my memory by constant repetition.

Yes, ladies and gentlemen, you fantasise impurity and cruelty while you speak of virtue and humanity. You claim to be civilised, but just look at the way you drive! If there were no traffic laws, or no likelihood of being caught if you broke them, what would prevent you from driving at a hundred miles an hour down a crowded street and mowing pedestrians down like skittles, so that you might arrive at the restaurant or for an appointment on time, or even for the sheer fun of it? Love of pedestrians in general, fear that you will injure them and that they will suffer as a result? Nonsense: for what are they to you, or you to them, that you should avoid them?

No, ladies and gentlemen, it is not love of your fellow man, but the fear of punishment, which keeps your foot off the accelerator. Fear is the prerequisite of order, and there is no civilisation without it. When fear is removed, what do you get: peace and reconciliation, or crime and chaos?

So, then, you live in fear; and fear is the mortal enemy of freedom. You feel trapped by it at every moment of your lives: which, of course, is why your fantasies are so extravagant.

But Dostoyevsky was an epileptic, a neuropath, you object: his ideas were almost certainly the result of a pathological electrical discharge in his brain. Besides, he was a Russian, and the inhabitants of such a morbid country are bound to have morbid thoughts.

I am surprised you display your vulgar prejudices so openly. Have I not repeatedly demonstrated that I am not the kind of man to be taken in by such speciousness? If Dostoyevsky's capacity to think had been destroyed, or even distorted, by a defect of his neurones, is it likely that he could have produced some of the deepest and most universal literary work of his, or any other, age? No, it is only because he writes something which disturbs your complacent equilibrium that you bring up the question of his epilepsy. As for the supposed morbidity of Russians, Turgenev was among the least pathological of the great writers, as was Chekhov. It is the truth of Dostoyevsky's words which you seek to deny by descent to the *ad hominem* plane of argument.

Besides, Dostoyevsky was far from the only one to recognise this truth. I quote from Louis-Ferdinand Celine:

> The first chance we get, we fall back on our old habits: massacre and torture ... Oh to be able to eviscerate someone! It is the secret wish of every 'civilised' person.

So what, you ask? Celine, you say (that is, if you are not completely ignorant), was a notorious fascist, a Nazi sympathiser. (And from where, from what source, do you suppose that Nazism sprang, I ask in parenthesis?) After the war, he had to take refuge in Denmark, and was only able to return to France after an amnesty.

But the truth of what a man says, ladies and gentlemen, is not to be so easily discounted. Even if the devil himself says so, are two and two not still four?

First, fascists had a good understanding of human nature. Did not fascism triumph originally in precisely the country of Europe with the longest continuous history of civilisation? And did it not next triumph precisely in the country of Europe with the highest level of education and culture?

Second, Celine spent many years in practice as a doctor. Thousands of secrets must have been reposed in him, and therefore there was nothing he did not know about the human heart. He knew whereof he spoke. That other doctors, equally the recipients of confidences, have not written in exactly the same terms demonstrates only the exceptional courage one needs to write the truth.

And this, ladies and gentlemen, is the key: you envy me, for I have liberated myself from the inner demons which still torment you, because you have not assuaged them. It cannot be that all the authors whom I have quoted – and many others whom I have refrained from quoting, since there is nothing more vulgar than a display of learning – are mistaken. No: it has long been appreciated that the first injunction of any ethical system, which was engraved over the entrance of the Academy in ancient Athens, is to *Know thyself.*

And I came to know myself after prolonged reading in the public library, and hard reflection in the solitude of my own home. I understood my capacity for violence and cruelty, not from personal experience, but from general principles which I derived from study. And I came to the conclusion (in common with all psychologists of repute) that you cannot repress a natural urge for ever: the very attempt to do so leads sooner or later to a pathological manifestation of it.

Take mourning, for example. Men and women who fail to mourn the deaths of those close to them eventually suffer a deep melancholia which may cause them to act irrationally, or at least to spend many years unproductively and miserably – all of which could have been avoided by the shedding of a few tears at the right time. I do not speak from experience, of course: I have never lost anyone close to me for the simple reason that no one has ever been close to me. But theoretical knowledge is still knowledge, even without direct experience.

Or take gluttony as another example. Who are gluttons? Very often you find that they are people who, in the first years of their lives, were denied the normal pleasures of food. And is the answer to gluttony total abstinence? Obviously not, because it is impossible. A man must eat to live, after all. The answer, then, is a compromise between total indulgence and total self-denial – something akin to Aristotle's golden mean.

And so it was with my urge to kill: I needed to find a golden mean. For ethical reasons I would not permit myself to perform what André Breton called 'the basic Surrealist act': namely, to go out into a busy street and shoot blindly into the crowd. Nor did I wish to suppress the urge to kill to the extent that it would one day emerge in that mad bellicosity and war fever by which all societies are seized from time to time, and which results in the deaths of untold thousands (or these days, millions), deaths moreover which occur almost entirely at random. Much better, I thought – and still think – to kill a few rationally selected individuals, chosen according to proper ethical principles, than to sink into such mindless degradation.

And in the process I became, for the first time in my life, a genuinely free man. Not, I admit, after the very first death, when I was still afraid that I might be caught, and perhaps not even after the second, when the fear lingered faintly, but after the third, definitely and definitively.

This was because, again for the first time in my life, I was acting purely of my own volition, and not in craven fear of what everyone else considered right, or in the hope of the paltry rewards which this society offers in return for conformity. I had decided on a course of action and had carried it out, like a completely free man.

Hence your envy, ladies and gentlemen, and why you have transformed me in your minds from a hero to a monster. For if you had not done so, what would disguise from you your own cowardice? What you proudly call your ethics is but the following of the herd, against your deepest and innermost inclinations. And that is why from time to time you have outbursts of terrible savagery, while I remain calm and collected at all times, even in the face of the most egregious insult.

For I have escaped the inner demons which still torment you.

8

I haven't quite finished with quotations yet: for though killing has had a bad press ever since Cain slew Abel (in Chapter 4 of the Book of Genesis), there have nevertheless been some partisans of the act courageous enough to brave the hypocritical censure of their fellow men. Political thinkers, of course, have always recognised the necessity on occasion to kill, whether they be pro or anti-revolutionary. But the kind of killing of which they approve is strangely abstract, as if it were not a question of one man ending the life of another, by shooting him or cutting his throat for example, but rather one of impersonal forces which kill without the need of a human intermediary. One suspects that the authors of such abstract bloodthirstiness would faint at the sight of blood, and complain that the civil war or revolution was interfering with their daily routine.

I shall not refer to those authors, naturally, who are full of sound and fury, signifying nothing (*Macbeth*, Act 5, Scene 5). Rather, I shall refer to those who have recognised individual acts of killing (I find myself obliged to use that emotive word for lack of another, more neutral term) as being psychologically reparative and socially constructive. And here, irony of ironies, I find myself quoting yet another psychiatrist, despite my general contempt for and aversion to the entire breed. But I am reassured by the fact that the words of Franz Fanon find no echo in the thinking of his colleagues – if, that is, the feeble movement of their minds can properly be called thought.

> Violence is a cleansing force. It frees the native from his inferiority complex and from his despair and inaction; it makes him fearless and restores his self-respect.

In killing his erstwhile master, says Fanon, a man recovers his power to act, and in the process becomes more fully and truly human.

I need hardly add, I suppose, that Fanon is not speaking here of the common criminal, of he who kills for lucre or in the middle of a quarrel with his common-law wife (these are the killers who generally find their way into our penitentiaries). Fanon does not approve of any killing whatever: it must be self-conscious and in pursuit of a great cause in order to possess the healing powers he describes. In short, the killer must possess high ethical standards, as do I.

If you have read Fanon, you are likely to ask how I can dare compare myself with the people about whom he was writing? He was speaking, after all, of the downtrodden masses of colonial regimes, while I (according to you) am, or was, a free citizen of a free country, able to do whatever I chose.

That's a joke! (You'll forgive me if I resort to a vulgar expression in a work as serious as this, but there are moments when spontaneity has its own value.) If I were to have stopped working, I should have found myself at once without an income, barely able to find enough to eat, and living in the perpetual cold and damp which are the worst consequences of poverty in a northern climate. How can you call it freedom to be thus forced go five times a week for twenty years to work which you loathe and despise, merely to stave off discomfort and wretchedness? Is freedom, then, the recognition of necessity, as Engels remarked? Be honest with yourselves for once, ladies and gentlemen, and admit that the only people who are genuinely free (and I mean free *to*, not merely free *from*), are the enormously rich.

Like almost everyone else, Fanon was a prisoner of his own experience, and therefore concluded that the oppression with which he had direct acquaintance was the only form of oppression which existed or could exist. That is how the mind of an intellectual works: egocentrically, with no imagination, and no sympathy for the predicament of others. Fanon would have dismissed as insignificant the oppression which I have experienced throughout my life, because I happen to have lived in a country which he would have called imperialist. But unlike him, I have had no Parisian Left Bank intellectuals to defend me in print, or to write on my behalf to the authorities.

The tyranny of everyday life is not the less tyrannous because it is concealed (on the contrary, concealment makes all tyranny the more difficult to bear); nor is it the less tyrannous because it is unimposed by water cannon, baton charges, torture chambers and the like. Nevertheless, life – except for the most privileged of the privileged – is a long series of the *diktats* of circumstance.

Think of your own everyday life: the illusion of freedom apart, is it not the case that everything you do from morning till night is dictated not by your own wishes, but by the demands placed upon you by society? Even the way you dress is laid down within very narrow limits, for those who would eat must have a job, and those who would have a job must dress in conformity with the expectations of their employers.

You wake not because you are rested, but because it is time to go to work, you eat not because you are hungry but because society has decreed that it is time to eat. In short, if you have the courage to examine your existence with the total honesty with which I have examined mine, you will admit that all your actions are constrained by the demands placed upon you by others, and that you are no freer than Fanon's downtrodden colonial peasant.

Thus the tyranny which 99.9 per cent of us experience is every bit as crushing as that described by Fanon; and thus it is as vitally necessary for us to overcome this tyranny as it was necessary for Fanon's so-called natives to overcome their inferiority complex *vis-à-vis* their colonial masters. And only the same means will suffice.

But who, you ask, is the enemy? Fanon's natives knew clearly enough; but we, who live in a Kafkaesque miasma, cannot point so easily to the authors of our oppression. The boss, after all, lives in the same moral swamp as we, and is no more free to act than we. His elimination would make no difference; he would be replaced immediately by someone with precisely the same characteristics. Besides, one would put oneself immediately at risk by disposing of one's boss.

But if there is no readily identifiable enemy, you will say, then Fanon's argument cannot apply to you (or us). How literal-minded you are! For it is the act itself of murder which liberates a man from his oppression, which makes him a *real* man for the first time in his life, one who acts from his own undiluted and uncontaminated will, and not the fact that he kills one person rather than another. It is the shooting of the arrow, not the finding of the target, which counts.

On what basis, however, is one to select those whom one is to kill, if not that of enmity? I have already stated my utter and irreconcilable opposition to killing at random, and it therefore follows that some principle or another must be employed by the man who wishes to transcend his condition of slave to the quotidian by means of murder.

I would have quoted Nietzsche, to the effect that the weak and ill-constituted should perish, and that we should help them to do so, were it not that you would dismiss the words of this philosophical genius as the ravings of a man whose brain, as is well-known, was rotted by syphilis, and who ended his days completely mute in an asylum.

Let me then quote to you the words of a man indisputably sane, a man who has been proclaimed a sage in his own lifetime, and whom I have read in the public library: Norman Mailer. Two young men beat the owner of a small shop to death, and Mr Mailer says:

> One murders not only a weak fifty year old man, but an institution as well; one violates private property, one enters a new relation with the police and introduces a dangerous element into one's life.

Yes, it's true that we all need risk or danger in our lives, though we need security as well. But where the author utters something genuinely profound is where he states that in killing a man one kills not just an individual, but strikes at an institution. For example, to kill a university professor is to weaken the university system itself. Indeed, on many occasions, I considered just such a 'victim': for how much have I suffered at the hands of those who considered themselves my superior merely because they attended a university and possessed a scrap of paper to certify that they were able during examinations to regurgitate faithfully what their professors had told them! And what had these professors done to deserve such slavish imitation? I grant that at some time in their youth or early adulthood they may have dabbled a little in research, and perhaps even found out something which was not known before (which is no guarantee of its usefulness, however), but the vast majority of them have settled comfortably into their sinecures, and consider themselves intolerably overworked if they have four hours' teaching a *month* to perform – while the rest of us spend more than sixty hours a week on our work, if, as is only reasonable, you count the time travelling to and from the place of our employment as work also. Yes, I should have liked to make an example of university professors as a breed – smug, underworked and overpaid, if you include all their perquisites – but prudence forestalled me: for professors are regarded as important people in this society obsessed by formal qualifications, and do not disappear without some notice being taken of the fact, not only among the self-regarding professoriate, but by the police. The cases would have been investigated to the best of the latter's admittedly limited ability, and before long I should have been apprehended, however elaborate my precautions. Thereafter I should have been unable to continue with the work: and I decided, therefore, that it would be better to choose less socially prominent 'victims'. After all, it wasn't as if the world was short of parasites worthy of elimination.

I can't entirely agree with Mr Mailer about private property, however. I suspect that *there* he is being a hypocrite: he disapproves of private property in the form of small shops but not in the form of writers' royalties and bank accounts. Supposing I had written to him to tell him of my hard and financially pinched existence, which prevented me from realising my artistic potential, and had asked for his assistance on the basis of his published opinion of private property as an institution. Do you suppose he would have replied with a cheque? I doubt very much whether he would have replied at all: or if he did, it would have been to pretend that he received too many such appeals to grant any of them. And if I had replied in turn that his refusal demonstrated that what he had written about his opposition to private property was a sham, a mere posture, and that logically speaking he should divest himself of everything he owned, I think it would have brought our correspondence to an abrupt end. No, Mr Mailer is sometimes capable of enunciating great truths, but by accident as it were: they do not emerge from a personality of transcendent moral scrupulousness.

But neither do I mean that private property in its present form is defensible: why should some people be allowed to earn in a day more than I earn in a month or even a year? Is it possible that there are people three hundred and sixty-five times (or three hundred and sixty-six times in a leap year) more talented, more intelligent, more valuable to society than I? I trust you will not reply with the cheap *ad hominem* jibe that I earned more in a week than a Bangladeshi or Zairean peasant earned in a year. Of course I admit that I earned more than such peasants; but the difference was less than you assume (or pretend). After all, if you divided my income by fifty-two, and asked someone to live on it in this country for a year, he would soon starve or freeze to death. But the Bangladeshi or Zairean peasant does neither of these things, *ergo* his income cannot have been a mere two per cent of mine. These peasants receive free heating, for example, as a gift of God. (I use the term God as a figure of speech, without any theological implications, and without prejudice as to his existence or nonexistence.)

Besides, you cannot sensibly judge a person who lives in one society by the standards prevailing in another. Poverty in a rich country would no doubt be counted riches in a poor one: but it is still poverty to the person who suffers it. Therefore, when I point to the injustice of the income differentials in my own country, between myself for example and (say) a young spiv in the City, or an equally young footballer, who have never been in a public library in their lives and would not know Kant from Spinoza, it is no answer that the differential is no greater than that between me and the inhabitant of one of the poorest countries in the world even supposing this were true, which it isn't, as I have demonstrated. Injustice exists within societies, not between them.

87

Of course, I am not saying that everyone should receive precisely the same income, far from it. Why should someone who does no work at all receive *gratis* an income from the state not so very different from my own, when I sacrifice five days of every week of my life to my work? What is the incentive for anyone to work in these circumstances? Absolute equality and the abolition of all property as advocated by the Mailers of this world would spell the end of effort, and moreover we should not be able to call even our teaspoons our own.

I am asking only for a fair crack of the whip, to allow myself for once the use of a cliche which nevertheless expresses precisely what I mean: the recognition that no man's labour can be worth hundreds of times that of another – at least, not that of a man who performs any work at all. How can the guitarist of a so-called musical group, with very limited talent and who after all is only entertaining people, usually very unintelligently, rightfully earn in a year or two enough to enable him to live in luxury for the rest of his life, when the vast majority of us will never experience such luxury, not even for a week or a day, however long we work?

In essence, I demand a scale of wages that is just and realistic: the best paid man, for example, should not receive more than twice or three times the amount that the worst paid receives. Nor should it be only a man's ability which determines his place on the scale: after all, ability is a gift of nature (I won't say from God, otherwise you'll think that I'm a believer, and as William of Occam pointed out a long time ago, in the fourteenth century to be exact, *entia non sunt multiplicanda praeter necessitatem*, which is to say that, philosophically speaking, entities are not to be multiplied unnecessarily, without good reason). No one can be said to deserve his own ability, therefore. Effort is thus a much sounder and more socially beneficial way of determining monetary reward, besides which the intrinsic unpleasantness of a task ought to be taken into account. If my scheme were to be implemented, it would result in a very different and much improved order of things: an order which represented a genuine moral hierarchy, and not the present egotistical anarchy, in which price is the only value.

Not that I expect anyone to take notice of my ideas, I am not so naive as to think it. A prophet is without honour not only in his own country, but in his own epoch.

Who, then, were my 'victims', as you persist in calling them?

Before I answer (I am not being evasive, you'll be told everything in due course, without reservation), I should perhaps explain the nature of my work. As I have already mentioned, I worked for twenty years in the Housing Department, and always in the same capacity: it was I who sat at the front counter of the Department, protected from the public by very necessary bulletproof glass, receiving requests for housing from the degraded, the desperate and the indigent. Those who were already housed by the Department wanted to be moved elsewhere, into the better accommodation of which they assumed, quite falsely, that it disposed.

There was a housing shortage in the town, of course, as there was everywhere else in the country: more applicants than dwellings. This fortunate circumstance gave the bureaucrats just the opportunity they needed. They developed a system of allocating of what they called *housing units* which was so complex and byzantine in its operations that more and more staff were needed to run it, so that the bosses were able to grant themselves ever grander titles for their own jobs. By the time I was arrested, almost everyone in the Department (above the very lowest level, that is) was a director or a manager of something or other. Some years before, a management consultant, the cost of whose hotel bill alone would have housed six families adequately for several weeks, had suggested that one way to revive flagging morale was to rid the Department of job titles implying the subordination of one person to another, and to create new titles emphasising the inestimable importance to the organisation of the bearer of them.

At the same time, the bureaucracy indulged in the pretence that it was accountable to the public whom it allegedly served. It instituted a complaints procedure (actually there was a Director of Complaints Investigation, a little weasel of a man called Jim Jimson, who kept a collection of pornographic material, as well as a quarter bottle of vodka, in his drawer), which itself was so difficult to understand that it effectively disposed of complaints before they could be made.

What an atmosphere prevailed in the office! Everyone was always on the lookout for some lapse or another on the part of their so-called colleagues to serve as the pretext for yet another meeting so that the office might be closed (temporarily, of course). I remember the meeting, which lasted two hours and grew very heated, as to what the preferred term for black coffee should be, since it had recently been decided by the Racism Awareness Officer that the word *black*, as applied to anything at all, was potentially inflammatory and degrading. I was howled down when I suggested that this discussion over the use of words was diversionary and trivial: the Savanorolas of the Housing Department then accused me of racism, and I lodged a complaint with the Director of Human Resources, alleging slander. Needless to say, I was completely vindicated. But it was nonetheless decreed that henceforth the correct usage in the office would be *coffee with* and *coffee without*, and that failure to apply these terms would be a disciplinary matter.

One day workmen appeared in the Department with instructions to affix pictures of great black men on all the walls. Such a portrait was hammered onto the partition of my little cubicle, which covered a smaller floorspace than the Director's coffee table (I am talking now of *the* Director, the Director of Directors as it were), but which was nevertheless known as my office. The portrait was of Mansa Musa, the Emperor of Mali who, according to the legend underneath, took so much gold in his baggage train on his pilgrimage from West Africa to Mecca that, *en route* through Cairo, the price of gold halved in the market there. We received a circular to inform us that removal of any of the portraits would be regarded as a dismissible offence. I protested that no authentic portrait of Mansa Musa could possibly exist, since Islam forbade the imitation of God's creation by representational pictures, and that this portrait was therefore a figment of a none-too-accomplished artist's imagination, to which an orthodox Moslem might object on strictly theological grounds; but of course my protest was ignored, it being impossible to argue logically with a semi-educated bureaucracy.

Indeed, we lived in fear in the Department: demons were conjured up to assure us of the significance of the least of our actions. You had only to look at a woman longer than a fraction of a second for her to accuse you of sexual harassment. And as soon as the accusation was made, the accused was suspended from work (on full pay, naturally) until an internal investigation was completed. This always came to nothing, since it was invariably one person's word against another's; but the accused and only partially-exonerated party might nonetheless be ordered to attend a sexual harassment awareness course (in working hours, naturally), run by a former employee of the Department, just to remove any lingering doubts in the office about his past and future conduct.

The only safe thing to be in the Department was a victim: and even the left-handers banded together and demanded a meeting to make everyone aware of the difficulties left-handers faced in a right-handed world.

They said that the latest research had proved that left-handers lived ten years fewer than right-handers, and that therefore they were entitled to early retirement, especially as much of the excess mortality among them was accounted for by their increased susceptibility to accidents brought about by equipment designed solely for the convenience of the right-handed, such as scissors. They demanded that henceforth at least the same proportion of equipment in the Department be adapted for lefthanded use as the proportion of left-handers in the staff or the population as a whole, a reasonable demand, they said, after several centuries of attempted suppression of lefthandedness by parents and teachers, who had tried to change children's handedness as if it were merely a matter of moral failure rather than of neurology and hence an integral part of a child's personality. The more extreme among the left-handed lobby demanded that an even higher proportion of equipment be adapted to left-handed use, claiming that a significant number of so-called right-handers were really left-handed, having been forced to change their preference in childhood, and that, with a modicum of official encouragement, they could be returned to their true identity, and hence to personal wholeness. They also said that restitution was only just and reasonable after so many centuries of oppression by the right-handed.

Left-handed scissors made their appearance for the first time in the Department, and a monitoring group was set up to check that they were available easily to those of the staff who might need them. But even this did not satisfy the lobby, which had scented blood: it pointed out that all the handles of the toilet cisterns were for use by right-handers, and demanded the installation of left-handed cisterns. And then it moved on to what it called *handedness-biased language*, the use of which it wanted to eliminate from the department: terms such as *sinister* and *gauche* which carried derogatory connotations concerning left-handers and lefthandedness, and were thus deeply wounding. Even the past participle of the verb *to leave* became suspect, since leaving is often sad and unhappy, and it was officially recommended that it should be avoided whenever possible. *He left his flat* should henceforth be written *He vacated his flat*, or even *He leaved his flat*.

And there were courses to attend – compulsorily, it goes without saying. I was sent three times in five years on a course on how to answer the telephone. It wasn't just a matter of picking the receiver up and telling the caller that this was the Housing Department: it was much more complicated than that. I spent three days practising the mandated reply: 'Good morning, the Housing Department, Graham speaking. How may I help you?' It wasn't just the words one had to get right, otherwise even the Director (who, of course, wasn't obliged to attend) could have learnt all there was to learn in a day: no, it was the correct intonation which was so difficult to capture, according to our instructors – also former employees of the Department who had struck out on their own. One had to remember that the person on the other end of the telephone was calling about a matter of the utmost importance to him or her, and therefore our voice must intimate by its tone a willingness to listen and understand. The tone required was somewhere between that of a clergyman taking choral evensong and that of a doctor informing his patient that he had advanced cancer.

But anyone who has ever telephoned the Housing Department knows that in practice things are quite different, and that a thousand courses on how to answer the telephone will not change them. We had two main techniques for discouraging callers: the first was simply not to answer at all. Eventually even the most desperate person gives up. This technique was not entirely satisfactory for us, however, because the prolonged ringing of a

94

telephone soon begins to get on one's nerves. It is a tough and determined man who does not succumb to temptation and answer it. A more satisfactory technique altogether was to answer the call immediately, thus putting an end to the irritation of the ringing, but to ask the caller before he or she could utter a word to hold on for a moment: a moment which could be almost indefinitely extended. And our Department being a large one, it was most unlikely that the caller had come through to the right person to deal with his case. If the caller had not rung off in despair by the time we took up his call again, it was possible to keep him waiting for yet a further period while we allegedly tried to connect him to the right person. The caller would hold on to his receiver, not knowing whether he had been cut off or not, until he concluded that he had been thus cut off and therefore he himself rang off. Another enquiry or complaint satisfactorily dealt with, from our point of view.

It was, of course, particularly gratifying to use these methods when the caller, having no telephone of his own, was in a public call box, for one knew then that he had wasted his assiduously collected coins on several minutes of silence, and that it would take him a considerable time, and a lot of effort, to collect so many coins again for a further attempt to contact the Department.

Do you conclude from this that the staff of the Department were fools and knaves? The former I am prepared to grant you, with very few exceptions: at lunchtime, all they spoke of was football and what they had watched on the television the night before, or what they would watch tonight. But let no one presume to judge them from the moral point of view who has never had to deal with the public *en masse*, day after day and year after year. For it is when you have worked with people that you learn truly to appreciate objects: the artefacts of Man being, as I have said before, so much more admirable than Man himself.

Yes, ladies and gentlemen, Man is a scoundrel. He is a cheat, a thief, a liar, a swine, a fool, a deceiver, a wheedler, a wife-beater, an oaf, a vandal, a lout, an ignoramus, a boor, a layabout, a moron, a bully, a coward, a drunk, a swindler, and a hypocritical whiner: in short, scum.

You go too far, you protest, you exaggerate, or at least generalise unduly. But which of us, I reply, has more experience of the human race as a whole, you who meet no one but members of your own class, or I who have encountered thirty people a day for twenty years, upwards of fifteen thousand in all? Which of us speaks with more authority on the subject of the human race, of human nature?

Because of this very nature, the extraordinary lengths to which the staff of the Department were willing to go to avoid individual examples of the species were unsurprising, indeed to be expected. When a mouse is confronted with danger, it freezes and starts to lick its paws; when a bureaucrat is confronted with the public, he holds a meeting. If only my so-called colleagues in the Department (who generally steered clear of me because of my broad intellect and sharp tongue, but who, just like my neighbours, affected the most intimate knowledge of me immediately after my arrest, their brief moment with a reporter or on television being the high point in their stunted lives) – if only, I say, they had been able to admit to their loathing for and disgust with humanity, how much more contented, how much less tormented, they would have been. Instead, of course, they had to pretend to love this humanity of yours, or even worse to serve it untiringly. Humanity itself, they were obliged to say, was good, and only the circumstances in which it found itself, created by the government, were bad. (By that, they meant *au fond* that their salaries were too small.) As I have mentioned before, not to recognise one's own true feelings, indeed to turn them into their direct opposite, is always dangerous: and to suppress them permanently in this fashion leads sooner or later to behaviour which is distorted and, as the psychologists put it in their desire to mystify the obvious, dysfunctional.

No one could truly and honestly have thought that humanity was good after working a week (let alone a year or a fifth of a century) in the Department, without doing the utmost violence to his immediate perceptions. And only a person of no judgment or sensibility at all could have failed to loathe humanity passionately after such a week. In fact, one would have to be profoundly depraved in one's tastes to like it after any intimate contact with it.

Of course, my superiors in the Department had been trained at university to deny the obvious, to assert the improbable and defend the indefensible, with all the sophistical arguments at their disposal. They – my superiors – could deny the hand in front of their faces, while indulging in theorising which had no conceivable relation to reality. Moreover, having achieved their promotion as rapidly as possible, thanks to their so-called qualifications, they withdrew from all contact with the public which they pretended to serve, thus enabling them to maintain their illusions. If you went to them with a particularly egregious example of vile behaviour by a member of the public, they would put the tips of the fingers of their two hands together as if in prayer, adopt a stage-compassionate tone of voice and tell you that what you had to remember was that these people (the public) were underprivileged, that they had never had any opportunity to succeed in life, that they were very poor, that most of them came from unstable backgrounds and broken homes, that many of them didn't even know who their father was, that they had probably grown up in an atmosphere of violence in which people got what they wanted by grabbing it or taking it forcibly from others, that they were badly educated because the schools were so underfunded and had leaking roofs (despite their allegedly higher education, my superiors always said *rooves*), that they had been unemployed for many years and were without hope of employment, thanks to the government's economic policies, and that their lives were boring and wretched: in short, that vile behaviour was a symptom of vile social conditions.

One might have thought my superiors were missionaries, they were so understanding and forgiving of the sins of the public. But just let one of them catch one of us returning from lunch ten minutes late, and see how understanding they were, these self-appointed guardians of compassion! They didn't care even if the reason for our lateness was that we had been attending the funeral of our closest friend or relative. The reason for their punctiliousness about our hours of work was not difficult to guess: they spent half their day with their feet up on their desks, reading the newspaper.

The way they spoke of the public – our *clients*, as they insisted that we call them, though they paid us nothing and were utterly powerless in their relations with us – you would have thought that they were not as fully human as, for example, were the upper echelons of the Department itself, but were mere automata whose appalling conduct registered their misfortunes the way the retreat of an amoeba's pseudopodium registers something noxious in the water around it. When they – the public, our *clients* – swore at us, it was because they knew no other language in which to express themselves or their so-called feelings; when they threatened us with violence, it was because the society in which they lived was violent. The fault was never theirs but only the system's: and only a revolution would put things right, but until then they, the upper echelons of the Department, would continue to draw their grossly inflated salaries, at least until it was time for them to draw their grossly inflated pensions.

How can I describe to you our 'clients' without drawing down upon me once again the accusation of exaggeration, an accusation so easily levelled by people with no experience whatever?

To begin with, they were physically repulsive, one and all. Their teeth were generally rotten, mere mottled black pegs by the time they were thirty. Well, you say, in your complacent middle-class tones of intellectualised but unfelt compassion, they couldn't afford dentists' fees. Humbug! I have visited hundreds of their houses, literally hundreds, to inspect them for the damp or the neighbour's noise of which they complain, and scarcely one of them is without a video cassette machine and compact disc player, often of the latest and most elaborate models, and most have computers with which they can while away their idle moments, that is to say their entire waking lives, by killing Martians who flood towards them on the screen to the sound of repetitive tinny music. Stolen, you say: all these videos were stolen, and were therefore not indicative of genuine choice. Well, I have yet to hear of anyone stealing to pay for a dentist; besides which, I ask how does it come that the pubs are filled night after night, with beer at more than a pound a pint? No, ladies and gentlemen, they don't go to dentists because they choose not to go, and because they are too improvident to do so.

They are either repulsively fat, or thin and runt-like – except, that is, the psychopathic young men who spend half their lives in a gym to get themselves fit for further violence. But if they are too fat, you say, it is because they eat too much junk food, and if too thin, because of continual smoking. In either case, it demonstrates the constant pressure under which they live. But what pressure, I ask, can make a man – with an infinitude of time on his hands, be it remembered, for he does not work, has not worked and has no intention of ever working – buy crisps and chocolate instead of lettuce and lentils? As for the smokers, I don't want to hear the stale nonsense about cigarette advertisements having influenced them: *I* have never smoked, and I have seen at least as many such advertisements as they.

And why don't they wash? The water flows from the tap for the rich and the poor alike, and soap is so cheap nowadays that even the poorest of the poor can afford it. The same goes for their clothes, which look as though they strain their food through them, and which smell of sweat and skin infection. Detergent, after all, is cheaper than beer or cigarettes.

As for the conditions in which they choose to live, they are deplorable. I say 'choose to live' advisedly, because there is no reason, other than sheer laziness and slatternliness, why their habitations should be so dirty, neglected and stained by every conceivable stain. Crumpled and unwashed clothes lie everywhere, scarcely in piles, but strewn like paint on a canvas of modern so-called art; the floors are covered with the detritus of everyday life, from crumbs to condoms, accumulated without tidying for weeks and months; the washing-up is left undone until a mouldy scum floats on the dregs in the cups; a dog has urinated on the sofa, or a bitch has given birth to pups on it; a large window pane is broken and has been replaced by a plywood board. But in every such household – give or take an illegitimate baby or two – there is one corner in good order, arranged with almost religious reverence. I refer, of course, to the corner in which stands the television and video (always switched on, it goes without saying), kept like a shrine or an ikon in a Russian peasant's *izba*. And every piece of furniture points to the holy corner: for it is the centre of the household's miserable existence.

What of it, you ask? An unemployed person has to occupy his time somehow, just like everyone else. This is precisely the point, ladies and gentlemen, that I wish to make: television occupies their minds. It is no coincidence that my metaphor should be a military one, for everything else is literally driven, fleeing, from their minds, however little there may have been there in the first place, to be replaced by the inconsequential drivel from which the television companies (or rather their shareholders) profit. Whenever I visited such a household, to check on the fungus which was allegedly growing up the walls (it never was) or on the roof which was allegedly leaking (only defects which could be blamed on the landlord interested them), I asked the complainant to turn off his television: but in many more than nine cases out of ten, and you have my personal guarantee that I no more exaggerate here than I do elsewhere in my narrative, to switch off a television meant to them no more than to reduce the volume of its sound. And it was futile to try to hold a conversation with them while the screen was winking silently in the corner: they were mesmerised, bemused, stupefied, bewitched by it. They had achieved that state of existence which the Zen Buddhists call *No mind*: and if you asked them what they had just been watching, they could not have told you, not for anything in the world.

I tried to avoid such visits, for obvious reasons. Our public housing is not pleasant, and to wander around it is risky and even dangerous. All the common parts (as we in the property business call them) are deeply impregnated with Saturday night urine, when the tenants and their friends cannot wait to reach the privacy of their own latrines to relieve themselves of their beery bladders. Anything which can be smashed has been smashed; obscene graffiti cover the walls. And of course, there is always the delightful possibility of being set upon by one of the many local gangs.

Oh, the things I discovered in tower blocks! There was a 'clinic' for female circumcisions run in William

Cobbett Tower by an unfrocked Sudanese doctor, to say nothing of the glue-sniffing necrophiliac orgies I unearthed in Ruskin House. No depravity is too depraved for an English housing estate, ladies and gentlemen. And everyone in tower blocks lives in abject terror of his neighbours. This is a world in which the most violent and unscrupulous man always gets his way, in which everyone else is afraid to put his nose out of doors even by daylight, but in which staying indoors is no guarantee of safety either. Not that many of the tenants want to venture outside in any case: for there was nothing there which could compete for interest, or at least for hypnotic power, with the flickering, swiftly-moving images of their televisions.

On average, my 'clients' watched twelve hours of television per day. Can this properly be called a human life, ladies and gentlemen? Does it not more closely resemble the life of those famous laboratory rats which have had electrodes surgically implanted into the pleasure centres of their brain, as a result of which they press the lever to stimulate the electrode to the exclusion of all other activity, even eating and drinking, until they die of exhaustion and inanition? Was the life of my 'clients' worth leading? Did not the ancients understand that the only life worthy of living was the life of the mind? I don't deny the needs of the body, ladies and gentlemen: but they should be met only so that the intellect be set free to soar into the realms of speculation. On earth, wrote Sir William Hamilton in his *Lectures on Metaphysics and Logic* (in the public library's reserve collection), there is nothing great but man; in man there is nothing great but mind.

And so my 'clients' were indistinguishable (except in one respect, which I'll come to in due course) from animals, from mere beasts. Their minds were empty, they watched television as sheep eat grass. But unlike sheep, they served no purpose for others. They produced

102

nothing, they gave pleasure to no one. I do not agree, of course, with the way sheep and other animals are raised purely for Man's pleasure, to be slaughtered at his convenience; but this does not affect the logic of my argument, which is that sheep, even if artificially raised and ill-treated, have a purpose and serve an end, though it be a disreputable one.

But what value did my 'clients' have? In my opinion, they had a *negative value*, if you will permit me a neologism. They were parasites, who consumed without producing. They absorbed everything provided for them like a sponge, but a sponge with a special quality: it could never be saturated. They ate and they were clothed at public expense: hence they drove up the price of commodities for the rest of us. They were the reason we had to pay such extravagant taxes, and why I had to work a third of my time (or receive only two thirds of my wages, I don't mind which way you want to put it) to support their worthless existence. And not only did they dispose of money which they did nothing to earn, but they had the luxury – which I have never enjoyed – of doing as they pleased the livelong day. Not for them the daily purgatory of rising while they were still tired, of performing a task which was odious to them: no, when they rose, usually at eleven in the morning, they stumbled over to the television to turn it on and fumbled with a cigarette to put into their mouths. They did not even have to dress if they did not wish to, and generally they didn't: at three in the afternoon, half of them were still in their nightclothes.

But if you consider them so fortunate, you ask, why did you not join them? It was not so easy to join this new aristocracy, this new leisure class. If I had resigned my post, ladies and gentlemen, the government would have said that I had voluntarily rendered myself unemployed, and would thereafter have allowed me only a pittance of a pittance; and even this they would have made conditional upon my acceptance of the first job offered me, which, because of my exemplary record of employment, would have been very soon after my resignation. No, you have to be born into the new leisure class, it is a true aristocracy; and my mistake was in having taken employment in the first place, which put me on the treadmill from which there was no escape.

But it was not only in consuming what they did not produce that my 'clients' did harm. In addition they were violent and criminal: if not themselves, then via their offspring. Many of them, indeed, encouraged their children in their criminality, sending them out to steal and burgle, because they knew that the law was so lenient and tenderhearted towards children that it would do nothing to punish them. There were, in truth, no practical or prudential reasons for these children *not* to have stolen.

You ask whether I have ever been the victim of a crime, that I should feel so strongly about it. Here again you display the superficiality of your thought, the habit of only looking at appearances. Let us pass over in silence the question of whether my house has ever been broken into, or my car taken and driven away: indeed, let us assume for the sake of argument that neither of these things has ever happened to me. But, like everyone else, I must take out insurance: and the level of the premiums is set by the level of claims. It takes no great insight to realise that a high number of crimes will lead to a high number of claims, and from thence directly to high premiums. No insurance policy is an island, entire of itself. Therefore, send not to seek from whom the thief steals: he steals from thee. (Adapted from Donne.) Moreover, no one can believe that the effects of a street robbery or a burglary are confined to the loss of property alone: the way one views the world is changed forever afterwards.

To what end is all this laziness, passivity and inactivity

on the one hand, and frenzied criminality on the other, put? Is it to lead a Socratic life of enquiry? No, it is to enjoy a purely animal existence completely devoid of the cerebration which makes Man truly Human. In killing such beings, one is not really destroying Human life at all: moreover, one is reducing the burden of public expenditure which weighs so heavily upon the rest of us.

10

Even so, you protest, it was not euthanasia you committed (and with which you were charged), it was murder. After all, the people whom you call your clients did not request death; and if they had been asked, they probably would not have wanted it.

But a pig or a cow does not want to die either, I respond, yet you kill it, or allow it to be killed on your behalf. Perhaps you will object that a pig or a cow cannot express in words its wish not to die, and therefore we cannot know that it objects to death, or even whether it has a concept of death. To which I reply two things; first, a baby or young child also cannot object to its own death in words, but you still take it as wrong to kill it. And second, a pig makes perfectly plain its objection to having its throat cut if given a chance to do so, not in words admittedly, but by squeals and other non-verbal actions. All the laws against cruelty to animals are predicated on the commonsense observation that animals can suffer, and can make their feelings known to us without the intermediary of language.

The point I am making, ladies and gentlemen, is the following: the mere expression of a wish by a living being not to die has never been taken as a sufficient reason in itself for not killing it.

Wait a moment, you say, proudly supposing that you have caught me out in a contradiction. Not long ago you were objecting to the killing of pigs: now you are using the fact that pigs are killed to demonstrate the permissibility of killing in general. Surely you contradict yourself?

Not at all. I did not object to the killing of pigs in any or all conceivable circumstances, only when the purpose of doing so is to satisfy temporarily the unhealthy gustatory lust for meat (unhealthy both physically and spiritually), especially among those who refuse to involve themselves in the messy and degrading business of the killing itself. I have never maintained that pigs have a right to life which overrides all other possible consider-ations. I do not hold a brief for the Porcine Liberation Front, if such exists, and I have never had any intention of going to the nearest pig farm to release all its pigs, in part because, had I done so, I should have provided the neighbourhood with a legitimate reason for killing them. Yes, if pigs were to become a common pest, if they were to break into our houses, say, and drive off in our cars, or attack us on the streets, which they roamed in packs and rendered unsafe at night, I should be the first to call for their elimination. If they covered our walls in graffiti, if they robbed old ladies outside Post Offices of their pensions, if they played their music so loud that the ground under your feet began to vibrate and your toes to tingle unpleasantly, if they smashed windows for the mere fun of it, and squealed obscenities at the top of their high-pitched voices, if they shoplifted and received stolen goods, if they urinated wherever they happened to be and especially in the entrances to buildings, if they got into vicious fights in pubs and demanded free legal representation afterwards, if they spent two thirds of their life in front of the television, and if they constantly conceived and gave birth to piglets without the least thought as to how they were going to maintain them or bring them up, then, ladies and gentlemen, there would be no one more anti-pig than I. On the contrary, I should found a vigilante committee, to protect the public from the depredations of these loathsome creatures.

Nevertheless, you stick grimly and – if I may say so doggedly, with the persistence of a man who is not accustomed to logical argumentation – to your prejudice that the wishes of a man should always be respected: he wishes not to die, therefore he should not be killed.

I have already examined the question of killing in times of war, and how your answer to it demonstrated that what you call your moral principles are actually mere unexamined prejudices. The plain fact is that desire of all the individuals in enemy armies not to die never stopped anyone killing them, or saved a single life. Irrespective of the rightness of killing in war, however, I will now examine your supposed principle that a man's wishes ought to be respected and complied with (in general, I do not like to end sentences with prepositions, but in the present instance I have no alternative).

It is an inescapable truth that millions of people – no, tens and hundreds of millions – have their wishes overruled each day, not once but several, indeed many times. I wish to leave my work to go shopping – I cannot. I wish to drink champagne every day – I cannot.

Trivial examples, you say. But, you continue, the right to life itself is a precondition of the fulfilment of all other wishes (except that to die, of course). And then you sit back with a smug, *quod erat demonstrandum* (Euclid: it would be tiresome to quote in the original ancient Greek, which I admit in any case is beyond my power) look on your face.

I shall now dent your complacency a little. There are many desires other than the desire to live which are anterior to the fulfilment of yet other desires, and yet they are not fulfilled or attended to in any special way. For example, all my life I have desired many things which required more money than I possessed: but no one ever suggested that I should be given or paid more money so that my subsidiary wishes should be fulfilled.

My point is logically a simple and unanswerable one:

what we wish for, and what we receive, are inevitably quite distinct.

Thus, I came to the conclusion (for I had given it much thought) first, that it was morally permissible to eliminate my 'clients', and second that it was obligatory, insofar as it fell within my means and capacity to procure this great public benefit.

There is, however, a difference between theory and practice, as observers of our system of government will have noticed, and there is always a reluctance to obey the dictates of conscience and conviction. How many Christians love their neighbours as themselves, let alone love their enemies? How many socialists give away their property to those less endowed with the goods of this world than themselves, or donate it to the government (as is permitted by law)? No doubt everybody in authority would have been much happier had I remained a hypocritical weakling, unable to act on my principles. A good example is always frightening. Fortunately, my daily contact with my 'clients' steeled my resolve. For they arrived every day with their specious, fatuous or arrogant demands, and turned unpleasant or vicious when they were refused.

In the allocation of public housing in Eastham there was (and still is, I should imagine) a points system: an applicant had to reach one thousand two hundred points to reach the top of the list. Unemployment counted sixty points; living alone counted another forty. An illegitimate child without paternal support also counted forty, while a second such child counted fifty. Alcoholism, drug addiction or a criminal record was worth sixty, while membership of a minority group was equal in value. It is unnecessary to continue with this enumeration, because if you have not grasped the principle on which it worked by now, you never will. A year on the waiting list, incidentally, counted for twenty points: in other words, a person who just wanted a house from the council might wait sixty years in the absence of any other factor working in his favour.

This was how it was supposed to work: unfortunately, all human institutions are fallible. Two factors entered to distort it: the first was the influence of the councillors and our bosses, who would descend with instructions that such and such a person was to be found somewhere to live immediately, without delay, whatever their ostensible lack of qualifications according to the points system, but whose lack of entitlement counted for nothing in the face of their acquaintance with or relationship to the councillors or bosses. And the second distortion derived from the conduct of the 'clients' themselves.

What were known as the normal channels, perhaps it is unnecessary to explain, were not torrential in their speed. I knew of cases which had not been closed, as we bureaucrats put it, for fifteen years. This dilatoriness was no more (or less) than the 'clients' deserved, of course, but some of them had different, and mistaken, views of their own just deserts. They grew impatient at what they considered a negation of their rights, and soon resorted to means other than filling in forms to secure them. I should perhaps mention here that it was standard procedure to lose the first copy of any application forms which a 'client' filled in, and then to deny all knowledge of ever having received them. This soon sorted out the serious applicants from those who were merely bored and had nothing else to do: the latter gave up after only one attempt. I do not say there was ever an official policy, laid down in writing, to lose the first application: but it happened so regularly, and so frequently by comparison with the number of times second applications which were lost, that it could be considered no accident.

I trust you will not succumb to the quintessentially English vice (sentimentality, which is the homage paid to feeling by indifference, a subtle – I think – adaptation of a maxim of la Rochefoucauld, namely that *L'hypocrisie est un hommage que le vice rend à la vertu*, hypocrisy is the homage which vice pays to virtue) and start to pretend to commiserate, at least in theory, with our 'clients'. The important thing to keep clear in your mind is that these people were morally entitled to nothing, to absolutely nothing. All the other facts of the case pale into insignificance by comparison with this cardinal fact.

But to return to those who were not satisfied with or by the normal channels: they resorted to the means which they saw succeed around them every day, namely the threat of violence. They were prepared to use real violence too: for every unmarried mother had in tow if not the father of her children or their latest stepfather, at least a male acquaintance of some sort whose powers of persuasion rested in his fists, his knife or his baseball bat. They – the unmarried mothers – were often enough on the receiving end of those fists, but this did not turn them against their use as a method: on the contrary, they only wished to turn them in another direction.

And so, when the demand of such an applicant was turned down, or her wishes not complied with at once, she would bring her violent lover to the Department who, as a first step, would glower menacingly at the Department's employee who was dealing with the case. Between them, they let it be known that if they happened to meet that employee outside the office – and they had all the time in the world to wait – it would be the worse for him. Moreover, they were soon able to discover which was his car: tyres were expensive to replace, and paintwork to respray.

Several members of the department had been assaulted by the 'clients', two of them receiving permanent injuries. One of the latter had been pinned against a wall by a car driven by an applicant's boyfriend, and her legs broken; the second had been hurled down an escalator in a busy shopping centre one Saturday afternoon, no one coming to his aid until the assailant, who screamed abuse at him for a time while he lay bleeding at the bottom of the escalator, had run away. This is the world we in the Department inhabited, ladies and gentlemen. And before you shake your head at the brutality of it in your habitually self-righteous way, may I ask you whether you would have gone to my colleague's aid or tried to apprehend the criminal? I should add that the assailant in this instance was six feet six inches tall, and an expert, as are so many of modern psychopaths, in what are called the martial arts. This, I maintain, is the consequence of feeding such people *ad libitum* and asking nothing of them in return: they have the strength of an ox, the brain of a chicken, and the morals of a hyena.

Is it any surprise that in these circumstances, those applicants who had such acquaintances, lovers, enforcers (call them what you will) found that their wishes were complied with in short order, and mysteriously acquired those twelve hundred points which brought them to the top of the waiting list? To boost their score, they were 'awarded' a couple of handicapped or illegitimate children, and a minority was found to which they belonged. And because they had been credited (if that is the word I want) with phantom children, whose existence was guaranteed by their written presence on file, accommodation had to be found for them with a sufficient number of bedrooms. The least uncultured among you will recognise Gogol (1802–1848) in this situation.

It goes without saying, almost, that the police would do nothing to protect us against the violence of our 'clients'. In their eyes, damage to our cars was a minor offence against property, not even worth their while to record, let alone investigate with a view to apprehending the perpetrator. Instead, they implied that it was our own fault for bringing our cars into so crime and vandal-ridden an area, and suggested that we used the bus instead. You don't go down into a snake-pit, as one police officer put it who came to speak to us about security, and complain about snakebite. In this phrase, he revealed what the police really thought of the inhabitants of the area: less than mammalian, let alone human. Why then did the same police call it murder when they arrested me, having belatedly discovered the bodies of my subjects? Surely culling would have been a better word?

The threats made against us, said the police, were such minor infractions of the law that prosecution was out of the question. And as for the assaults themselves, no one was willing to testify against a psychopath who, if convicted, would be let off with a mere admonishment not to do it again, or at most a fine.

Even without violence, however, I was subjected to the most intense provocation. What else can you call the wilful and deliberate stupidity of my 'clients', to say nothing of their rudeness? Each of them came with an impossible demand: to be moved somewhere where people like them did not live. Each of them laboured, or pretended to labour, under the same delusion, namely that the Department disposed of accommodation in which decent people lived, where neighbours did not totally disregard each other's comfort and therefore did not play rock, rap or reggae music at a volume of a trillion decibels at three o'clock in the morning, and certainly did not break the ribs of anyone who dared complain about it. No, wherever the Department had property, there were drug pushers and prostitutes on the street corners, and rapists lurking in the shadows.

Each day I supposed that I had finally plumbed the depths of human folly and depravity, but on each succeeding day I learnt that these human characteristics were truly fathomless. The day I came to my decision –

113

not without agonising – a man threatened to knife me on my way home.

'You won't be behind that fucking glass for ever,' he snarled, putting his face against it so that I could see the coarsened, greasy pores of his skin, widened by years of alcoholic overindulgence.

He had demanded a three bedroomed house.

'I've got ten dogs,' he said. 'You can't expect me to go on living for ever in a one bedroom flat.'

But this does not count as real provocation, you say – you, who have never dealt with the public as a servant, but have only been served. What, may I ask, would you condescend to call a provocation? According to the law, you reply, provocation (to count as an excuse) must be immediate and moreover the reaction must be without premeditation, a dish served hot rather than cold.

Again I reply with a two-pronged argument: first that the law has changed, and therefore your ideas are out of date, and second that even if the law's doctrine had remained petrified in its antiquated, indeed mediaeval, psychology, I am talking in this work of moral, not mere legal, responsibility.

It is now accepted by every intelligent person that provocation may be chronic as well as acute. You must have read in the newspapers of a recent case in which the wretched wife of a vicious husband killed him in his sleep. From the very outset of the marriage, he had behaved to her with exemplary brutality: and she shot him while he snored. She could not have claimed to act in self-defence, since at the moment she killed him she was in no danger from him. Neither was she provoked in the immediate sense, unless snoring be considered sufficient. Yet the courts accepted that she had been provoked beyond endurance, and she walked free from the court to the self-congratulatory applause of the nation, proud of its quality of mercy (*The Merchant of Venice*, Act 4, scene 1).

114

Is my case, I now ask you, so very different? True, I was not persecuted by a single person: instead, I was persecuted by a whole class of persons, my 'clients'. And is it worse, I ask you again, to be persecuted by one or by many?

The provocation was constant, unceasing and intense. You will, perhaps, maintain that it was not physical as in the case of the excused female murderer: and I admit that even if I received threats, I was never actually attacked in person, unless you count thumps on the counter and the flinging at me of pens and any other objects which came to hand, but which fortunately always bounced off the thick, reinforced glass which separated the staff from their 'clients'. The distinction between physical and verbal assault is in any case a false and artificial one, yet another example of a distinction without a difference, as the philosophers put it. For how is a threat to be communicated except through language and gesture, both of them events every bit as physical as a punch in the face? When I implied that I had never been attacked physically, I was using, of course, the language of the philosophically naive and uneducated man in the street.

But even if, for the sake of argument, one were to grant the validity of the distinction between a threat and a physical assault, there is a further point to consider: that the law, in this instance quite rightly, though more by good luck than judgment or a desire to do justice, does not assume that any physical assault is worse than any merely verbal threat. A fracas in the pub leads to a fine at most, even if blood is spilt; but a threat to kill results in a five-year sentence at the least. And this is as it should be, since a fracas, once over, is likely to be forgotten, while a threat lingers in the mind, and destroys the peace of mind of the person who receives it for a long time to come.

And does not the law recognise mental cruelty as

grounds for divorce? Is physical suffering (I am resorting once more to the language of the man who lives the unexamined life, that is to say the immense majority) the only kind we recognise? I am not trying to minimise the horror of torture when I say that some of the worst suffering known to Man arises through the power of mental representation, and not at all through physical hardship or illness. A man may deem his life not worth living, though he live surrounded by comfort or even luxury (is not suicide more common among the upper classes, particularly among doctors?). By contrast, a man may be wracked by disease, in constant pain, and poor into the bargain, and yet hang on to his life as on to something precious. No, ladies and gentlemen, the relationship between suffering and those events or processes commonly called physical (as if there could be events or processes of any other kind) is by no means unequivocal.

The matter of suicide among doctors is worth examining in a little more detail, for it bears a relation to my case. Why do doctors kill themselves in such comparatively large numbers? Because, you reply glibly, they know how to do it, and moreover have the means to hand. Come, come, ladies and gentlemen, surely even you can think of something better than that! We live surrounded by buildings of great height, egress from whose roof or windows is available to all without the exercise of great ingenuity or perseverence. Our chemists' shops are full of lethal substances on the sale of which there are absolutely no restrictions, and we inhabit an island much of whose coastline is formed by cliffs of great height, which are never more than a hundred miles distant from us. Rope is easily obtained, and no building in the country is without fitments from which it is possible to suspend oneself by the neck. The entire country is electrified, and it requires so little knowledge of the properties of electricity to kill oneself with it that even our uneducated and ignorant population must surely be able to do so if it so wished. Trains criss-cross the countryside at more than a hundred miles an hour, and the tracks are all too easy of access; there are bridges over deep waterways (more than a score of them in London alone) within everyone's reach. And all public libraries have several textbooks of pharmacology, from which implicit instructions for self-destruction may be derived.

I think I have demonstrated sufficiently that superior technical knowledge and access to drugs do not explain the phenomenon of self-destruction among doctors. One does not, after all, require much knowledge of physiology to understand that defenestration from twenty storeys up is deleterious to the health.

Nor can it be said that doctors are by nature unstable men, that the germ of suicide lies dormant within them from an early age. On the contrary: the great majority of the strenuous studies imposed upon them at medical school are quite redundant, perfectly useless from the practical point of view, and are more a *rite de passage* or even a trial by ordeal than education properly so-called. No one can deny the strenuousness of these studies, whatever their pointlessness, and to complete them requires considerable psychological stability – as well as burning ambition, snobbery and greed, of course.

No, the doctor's impulse to kill himself comes from elsewhere: in short, it comes from you, the public, ladies and gentlemen. Prolonged and inescapable contact with the human race, of which you are undeniably a part, with its frivolous but time-consuming demands, its adamant refusal to take responsibility for itself, its bad manners, its lack of elementary personal hygiene, its improvidence, its ignorance and stupidity, its meanness, its bad taste and triviality, drives doctors to despair and hence they kill themselves.

But there is all the difference in the world, you say,

117

between killing yourself and killing others. I agree that there is a difference, but not of the kind you think. And this difference can be boiled down to one word: cowardice. Perhaps I should have said two, or even three, words: cowardice, sentimentality and hypocrisy.

Explain yourself! you demand. I shall. The doctor, whatever his secret lust for power, wealth, social position and so forth, must cloak his whole mentality in a mantle of benevolence and philanthropy. Even to be admitted to medical school, he must feign an unnatural concern for the welfare of others, and this pretence continues throughout his entire professional life. Eventually, if one plays a part for long enough, it becomes such an important component of one's personality that it holds the rest together; and if, for some reason, one ceases to play it, the personality disintegrates altogether.

Now the doctor, to maintain the illusion of his universal beneficence upon which he had predicated his life, must pretend (to others, but above all to himself) that every person who consults him, however objectionable, agressive, dirty or unmannerly, is only a suffering soul worthy of sympathy who deserves his compassion. He must deny appearances and see in the undesirable qualities of his patients not their essential evil, but an inevitable expression of something else, whether it be an illness, an unhappy home life, a low income, unblameworthy ignorance, or a lack of intelligence consequent upon childhood malnutrition.

The strain of trying to believe all this proves too great. Eventually the sheer weight of appearance overwhelms the theories which the doctor uses to disguise them, and the elaborate, rigid but brittle intellectual edifice with which he has protected himself against reality shatters utterly. But even at this late stage the doctor cannot abandon his role of universal philanthropist altogether, for to do so would be to question the purpose of the

118

whole of his past, whose frustrations and tribulations, far from having been endured for the sake of a higher purpose, now appear to have been endured in pursuit of a lie. Torn between two *Weltanschauungen*, he takes his revenge not upon those who have caused his misery, but upon himself.

I trust I do not have to spell out the similarities between the doctors' situation and my own. I, too, had to deal with the footling demands of the public day after day in the name of benevolence. I, too, had to deal with the importuning, the wheedling, the menaces, the lies, the illiteracy, of man in the mass. But unlike doctors, ladies and gentlemen, I did not undergo a lengthy training to divest myself of the ability to perceive the truth, to mystify reality in clouds of theorising, and to deny my own innermost and truest feelings: unlike doctors, I have not had my self-knowledge destroyed. I hated my 'clients', and I was not going to play their game by killing myself. If I was miserable, much better – more honest, more rational, more *useful* – to remove the sources of my misery than end my own life.

But, you object, though you removed some of the sources of your misery, it was still only a small minority of them, who – as you yourself pointed out not long ago – numbered many thousands over the years. To kill fifteen (or twenty-two, if we count those cases ignored by the police) was unlikely to make any practical difference to your life. For the class from which your 'victims' (that word again!) were drawn is hydra-headed.

What a crudely rationalistic conception of life you have, ladies and gentlemen! Is not Man *par excellence* (I cannot think of an exact English equivalent, and therefore the foreign phrase is perfectly acceptable in this context, and not at all an ostentation) – is not Man *par excellence* the being for whom symbols are all-important? Wars have been fought over symbols: and is it not common experience that men grow angrier over words than over the things themselves that the words supposedly represent?

I could not, it is true, hope to eliminate the whole class of my tormentors, but surely it will be conceded that the deaths of fifteen of them (or, *a fortiori*, twenty-two) had some symbolic value. And each man can reasonably be required to do only what falls within his power to do. If everyone who had the opportunity to act as I acted were to do so, the world would soon enough be cleansed of those whom Dean Swift (before he went mad, be it remembered) so eloquently and accurately described as 'the most pernicious race of little odious vermin which nature ever suffered to crawl upon the surface of the earth'.

It was the provocation under which I acted which allowed me to plead diminished responsibility. I admit that I had qualms about so pleading – in case it detracted from the public understanding that I acted both in accordance with morality and in a public spirit – but my lawyer insisted. In my all too easily comprehensible confusion of the time, I deferred to his judgment.

11

The judge, on the other hand, made much of the fact that I planned my acts with the greatest care. How else he would have expected anyone to carry them out I do not know. He dismissed the idea that I was provoked, and then, in full contradiction of himself, suggested that I acted from a desire for revenge. What does this tell us, ladies and gentlemen, about his intellect, the much vaunted so-called intellect of the English judiciary? For if I was not provoked, what was there to revenge?

I have never disguised the fact that I wished to punish my tormentors and make them pay for the suffering they inflicted upon me – at least, I have never disguised it since the discovery of the bodies in what the tabloid press, with typical overstatement, called my garden. A man who has acted morally disdains to conceal his motives.

Nor have I ever concealed the pleasure afforded me by my activities. I do not mean the killing itself: I found it rather tedious and tiresome, in fact. I am no sadist, having overcome my childish and adolescent propensities in that direction a long time ago. The mere throttling of my 'victims' gave no pleasure at all to me, and the disposal of their remains was, frankly, a disagreeable chore. No, my pleasure was an altogether subtler thing, richer, more intellectual and ethical in nature: the realisation that the world now contained one fewer unworthy person to consume its scarce resources to no other end or purpose than the very consumption itself.

I admit, however, that the search for and choice of 'victim' was not without its pleasures, the pleasures of the chase. For a mistake in the selection could have been fatal (if I may be allowed that word in this context) to the whole enterprise. A challenge, then: and who does not like, or rise to, a challenge?

I had always to find a person of the right characteristics: someone who lived alone, who either had no relatives or who had so alienated them that all contact had been broken off, who was unemployed and who led the kind of isolated existence such that his or her disappearance would arouse no curiosity or would not even be noticed, or if noticed would be attributed to a desire to move and leave no trace behind – a desire common enough in this class. And although my initial impression had been that there were many such people to choose from, when I looked into the matter more closely, the great majority of possibles turned out to have a defect from my point of view: a grandmother whom they visited once every two months, an old boyfriend who turned up every time he came out of gaol, or merely once in a while (when he needed a meal or sexual intercourse), a neighbour with whom they were carrying on a feud which had become the neighbour's *raison d'etre*, or an illegitimate son at a boarding school for the behaviourally disturbed who came home during holidays.

A single small error could have ruined my project and therefore I had to proceed with the utmost caution, which explains my relatively low level of activity over the years, if I may put it thus. I had no illusions as to my ability to clear the world entirely of human parasites, but I wished to rid it of as many as possible, which naturally entailed remaining undetected for as long as possible, if not indefinitely. I also knew that it was likely I should be caught in the end, but I was willing to brave martyrdom for my cause.

It wasn't only a question of selecting the right candidates, however. In a way the selection was the easiest part because, as a distributor of points for the housing list, I had the right – indeed, the duty – to ask members of the public the most intimate of questions concerning their lives. I even asked about their sexual practices, and they did not think it odd or impertinent. In the event, several of my 'victims' were pregnant, and these, of course, gave me double pleasure, insofar as prevention is better than cure. Some of you, perhaps, may find it strange that a pregnant woman could have fulfilled my criteria as a candidate (social isolation etc.), but your surprise only demonstrates how far you are from understanding the nature of my 'clientele' or of the world they inhabited: for a pregnancy was of no greater significance in that world than was buying a stamp at the post office, catching the bus or switching the station to which their television was tuned.

But having selected a candidate for elimination in the public interest (be it remembered) was one thing, carrying out the elimination in practice was quite another. First I had to gain his or her confidence so that I could lure him or her safely – from my point of view, that is to say – to his or her death. It was not usually very difficult: I had merely to feign sympathy towards their requests or demands, in itself so extraordinary and unexpected a stance in an offical of the Housing Department that they at once dropped their guard. All I had then to do was to maintain that, though their case was undoubtedly among the most deserving I had ever known, the procedure to bring about the desired result was of such complexity that I could not hope to complete it during normal working hours. So deep, however, was my sympathy with their cause that if they came to my home in the evening, I could and would complete the necessary paperwork there.

Of course, their timekeeping left a lot to be desired:

they were, after all, people to whom time meant nothing, except perhaps the approach of a television programme or a payment from Social Security. They would invariably arrive late for their appointment, so that I had to counteract this tendency by giving them an appointment for an earlier time than I intended that they should arrive. Sometimes they arrived – perhaps turned up would be a better way of putting it – on the wrong day altogether. When I pointed this out to them – gently, for I did not wish to alarm them or frighten them away at this stage in the proceedings – they did not apologise, but on the contrary, provided me with a whole cascade of fatuous excuses, all of which were entirely egotistical and took no account at all of the convenience or well-being of others such as I. This, naturally, reassured me that I had chosen my subjects not only wisely but with great accuracy.

It wasn't difficult to put my subjects to sleep with a drink spiked with capsules I had procured from the doctor. So much for the so-called clinical acumen of the medical profession, which was quite unable to distinguish between a true insomniac and a man who wanted to use his prescription to lull his subjects to sleep before they died.

As was only to be expected, the drug did not work at once, especially as half my subjects were taking it already: insomnia being a common consequence of the boredom of a pointless existence. There was a dangerous interval between the taking of the drug and the sleep it induced, during which I could not afford to let my subjects depart in case they later realised their drink had been spiked and then went to the police with the information. Though I was not, and am not, a man of violence, I had a baseball bat at the ready, forcibly to oppose and prevent their departure. They were all too familiar with the use of this implement, as I think I have already mentioned, not as sports equipment – no one played baseball within a radius of fifty miles – but as a means of acquiring property and getting one's own way. It was they, in fact, who had taught me as the use of such a bat as a weapon.

Fortunately, though, I never had to use it. I imagine that I should have found the impact of the wood upon the hard but brittle skull, or on the maggot-soft abdomen, distasteful and even revolting. No, though I am an unsocial man (and there is a world of difference between being *un*social and *anti*social), I can charm and amuse when I want or need to do so, and I managed to keep my subjects cheerful and contented until sleep overtook them.

Now came a difficult moment – not difficult morally, I had settled all that in my mind already and was at ease with myself – but difficult physically. As I believe I may already have mentioned, I am not powerful or muscularly well-endowed, and I freely admit that I have no presence: I am the kind of man who can walk into a room without anyone noticing. It is not surprising, then, that I am not especially strong, though I am what is known as wiry, and strength is a distinct advantage in a strangler. Asphyxiation is more difficult than you imagine to carry through to a successful conclusion, and not only because, even when unconscious, a struggle is put up by a subject. Sometimes one mistakenly believes that the subject has stopped breathing and its heart has stopped beating. You may believe me, ladies and gentlemen, when I tell you that there is scarcely a more terrifying experience in the world than the sudden revival of one whom one believes one has successfully strangled and who should therefore be dead. Fortunately, I kept my head when it would have been all too easy to lose it and then to flee in panic – and a lesser man might have done so. I returned to the fray and emerged victorious: and I learnt also the difficult lesson that death is not always as easily distinguishable from life as one might have supposed.

125

The most difficult part of all remained, of course: the disposal of the no longer living. However, this is not the place to go into practical details, for to do so would detract from the force of my argument. This is, after all, a philosophical work, not a do-it-yourself manual. Perhaps one day, when I am more at leisure, I shall write a guide to the disposal of human remains, but for the moment I prefer to confine myself to more important, though admittedly abstract, matters. I am not seeking to interest or amuse those who thrive on cheap sensation.

I cannot, however, forebear to mention the exquisite joy (not to be confused with relief) I felt once my task had been completed. To have served the public and to have released myself from the inhibitions of a lifetime: I have known no satisfaction to compare with it. I always slept soundly afterwards.

But when the judge said at my trial that I acted from a wicked desire for vengeance upon a world which had disappointed me, his upper lip curled at the very word *vengeance*, as if he were speaking not of a universal and inevitable desire, a human constant like hunger or thirst, but of something disreputable or even repulsive. Here again, ladies and gentlemen, we see the formidable power of self-deception: for what is all judicial punishment except a licensed form of vengeance, administered coldbloodedly by those who themselves have suffered no injury from those upon whom the revenge is wrought?

The judge, in the unlikely event that he were ever to read this, his mind being firmly closed against all new experience, would protest vigorously that legal punishment is much more than mere vengeance, and maintain against all the evidence that it performs several important social functions at once, among which are protection of the public, deterrence, correction and rehabilitation of the wrongdoer, *et cetera*. And all of you would nod your heads in agreement and approval.

Let us examine the matter a little more closely, ladies

and gentlemen. I shall not stoop to mention again – because it would be a cheap debating point to do so – the late Chief Justice, who lived and passed sentence within my lifetime, who derived sexual gratification from pronouncing the death penalty. Nor shall I be so foolish as to deny that the incarceration of recidivists – of burglars, say – does, by definition, protect the public for a time from their depredations. Remember, I am what I have always been, a genuine searcher after Truth.

But the proof that vengeance is not merely divine, but a fundamental principle of English law, resides in the latter's treatment of those whom I may (I think) call *domestic murderers*. By domestic, I mean the killing of a spouse in a moment of ungovernable, or at least ungoverned, rage, after the discovery of adultery or other affront to the murderer's *amour propre*.

Study after academic study has demonstrated that these men (for most of them are men) are unlikely ever to commit another crime. Most of them have never committed a crime before they killed their wives, either. So punishment as reform is out of the question, since there is nothing to reform; likewise the public has no need of protection from them. This leaves deterrence and vengeance as the two possible motives for sentencing them not merely to imprisonment but to imprisonment for life. With regard to deterrence, no one has ever been able to produce the slightest evidence that any punishment whatsoever, even the death penalty itself, actually deters the act of murder. After all, if deterrence had worked, would any men ever have killed their wives? Were not their passions at the time of their deed not so inflamed that they were no longer capable of considering the consequences of their own actions? No, ladies and gentlemen, a man does not weigh the *pros* and *cons* of killing his unfaithful wife before doing so, and only someone completely without insight into the workings of the human heart (a metaphor, for I am far from

127

supposing that the heart is the actual anatomical seat of the emotions) could imagine that he did. Thus, regardless of the penalties, there will always be some men who kill their wives, and hence the argument for imprisonment as deterrence collapses like a house of cards.

Which leaves vengeance.

I have already explained that the locus of moral authority cannot be the state, a principle established at Nuremberg. Therefore, if it be permissible for the state to exact vengeance, it must be permissible for individual citizens to do likewise. *A fortiori*, in fact: for while citizens as individuals may truly experience the real and genuine emotions which justify vengeance, the state, being an abstraction, cannot possibly do so.

Moreover, the judge, in ascribing to me a single motive only, fell prey to the absurd fallacy that human actions have a single unique and final cause which explains them to the exclusion of all other explanations. If I acted from a desire for vengeance, he argued (or rather implied), then I could not also have been motivated, as I always said I was, by the desire to perform the public some service. But, My Lord, if one as humble as myself may be permitted to apostrophise for a moment one as mighty and important as yourself, consider your own behaviour: has it always one, and only one, motive? And if not, if your behaviour has several motives, should it always be ascribed in the last analysis to the least creditable of these several motives? Let us give you the benefit of the doubt, and suppose that you love justice and wish to see it triumph everywhere; does this mean you are obliged to forgo your salary, lest your love of justice be contaminated by the love of filthy lucre? No, My Lord, just as a man can love justice and yet still accept payment for administering it, so can a man desire to serve the public and be revenged upon his tormentors at the same time.

Nor did the judge confine himself to remarks about

128

the supposed incompatibility of public and private motives (as if they could ever be disentangled!). He felt free to animadvert as to my character in general. As far as I know, no one has ever protested at the gross natural injustice of this inequality in the rights granted a judge and the accused. But if the character of a man undergoing trial may be investigated and then traduced in court – that is to say, in public – then surely natural justice requires that the character of the man conducting the trial should be subjected to the same jeopardy. No doubt you will reply with the hypocritical fiction that the accused has his voice in court, even though it be a surrogate one in the form of his counsel; but the latter plays by the rules of the game, and his first loyalty is to the game rather than to his client. Indeed, his livelihood depends upon obedience to these rules, for fear of expulsion from the game. Not only does a man's counsel fail to say in court all that he would like him to say, he specifically refuses to do so and resorts to threats (to abandon the case in mid-trial) if his client should insist upon his saying something he deems inadvisable. And the rules of the game, which are opaque to everyone except the lawyers themselves (which is how they maintain their indispensability, after all), are specifically designed to prevent the accused from using every argument relevant to his case, for fear of causing embarrassment to his accusers.

The judge, taking cowardly advantage of his immunity to criticism, referred – with his pendulous and moist lower lip quivering, as if in anticipation of something really tasty – to my deliberate wickedness. I could see several of the jurors, not a few of whom looked as honest themselves as bookmakers at race meetings, nodding fervently in approval.

The fools! Could they not see that the phrase *deliberate wickedness* was itself the product either of the judge's animus against me – so much for his supposed neutrality!

– or of a deeply impoverished intellect, despite the many years of training it had supposedly undergone? For how, I ask you, could wickedness be other than deliberate? Try the phrase with the opposite meaning: accidental wickedness. It will be understood at once by almost everyone that, since this phrase is a contradiction in terms, its opposite must contain a redundant word, to wit *deliberate*.

Now either the judge knew this, or he did not. If he knew it, he was guilty of resorting to a vulgar rhetorical device, in which case he was not a fit person morally to conduct my trial (or that of any other person).

If, on the other hand, he did not know it, if he really thought that the use of the word *deliberate* in connection with wickedness was not supererogatory, then his intellect was not up to the task of conducting a trial properly. (Is it not extraordinary, by the way, that there should be no requirement in our legal system for jurors to be at least of a certain level of intelligence and education, especially in cases such as mine which are not straightforward and which require philosophical sophistication?)

When I pointed out to my lawyer that in either case the judge was not competent to deliberate upon the fate of another, that is to say me, and that this single phrase of his demonstrated that I had not received a fair trial, he remained, or pretended to remain, unmoved. This, he remarked superciliously, was not sufficient grounds for an appeal either against verdict or sentence: but if the moral or intellectual incapacity of the judge is not sufficient grounds, I should like to know what is.

And now I should like to enquire a little more closely into what the judge meant, or thought he meant, when he used the word *deliberate*. That, at least, is easy, I hear you say: *deliberate* means *knowingly, of your own free will*.

Yes, for you everything is clear and easy, ladies and

gentlemen. That, I venture to suggest, is because you do not take the trouble to think very hard, or to be critical of your own conceptual framework. Perhaps you will plead in your own defence the press of everyday business – work, shopping, taking the children to school, putting them to bed, and so forth. And I grant that, unlike me who has enjoyed the benefits of social isolation and therefore of increased access to the public library, you have not had the leisure, even if initially you had the inclination, which I doubt, to examine your own ideas from a philosophical standpoint. But this being the case, I deny you the right to stand in judgment over me for even so much as an instant. A man should be tried by his peers, not by his intellectual inferiors.

Now, however, that I have raised the issue of free will, you have no further excuse for not considering it as deeply as you can. And I ask you now what you mean by the words *knowingly* or *of your own free will*? You may take the coward's way out, and reply that these concepts are irreducible to any others, and therefore not susceptible of further analysis: in which case I congratulate you, ladies and gentlemen, for having discovered – merely by the repetition of your own prejudices – elements in the universe more fundamental by far than the tiniest and most recently-discovered sub-atomic particles. For nothing has a final cause, ladies and gentlemen, unless it be God Himself (if he were to exist, that is, which at the least is open to doubt) and I take it that you do not consider men – the possessors of your precious so-called free will – to be so many gods, all equal to the one God?

What is it, this will that you deem to be free? Take the thought that is currently occupying your mind, whatever it may be. Where did it come from, did you conjure it to come into your mind by an act of choice? The answer must be no, ladies and gentlemen, because otherwise all the thoughts you ever had, have now and will have must

131

be already present in your consciousness, simultaneously, which I take it you will agree to be an impossibility. Likewise, you will acknowledge that your every thought arises from sources of which you know nothing.

Moreover, thought is the father of action, or at least of all action which is above the level of a Pavlovian reflex. It follows that the source of all our actions must remain unknown to us. This being the case, can any action be said to be deliberate, in the sense in which the judge meant it, that is to say, freely and consciously chosen? And if again the answer is no, can anyone be held personally responsible for anything? We none of us know why we act as we do, and therefore have no right to sit in judgment over each other.

Indeed, what is the *I* and this *You* which is so ceaselessly, and yet so carelessly, invoked? I have no wish to make a vulgar exhibition of my erudition, but it is surely significant that as long ago as Heraclitus (his exact dates are uncertain, but in any case irrelevant in this context) it was pointed out that the same river cannot be stepped into twice. Heraclitus meant by this, naturally, that by the time anyone returned to the river into which he had once stepped, it had changed to such an extent because of the flow of its water, the erosion of its banks and bed, etc., that it could no longer be called the same river. Someone, I admit that I forget who, and the prison warders are hardly the people to ask, extended the argument even further, to its logical conclusion: you cannot step into the same river once.

Applying the argument of Heraclitus to the question of personal identity, is it not evident that there is no such entity as the persisting *I* and the persisting *You*? Physics and physiology alike teach that the molecules which make up the human form are in constant motion, and that not a single molecule with which a human organism started out in life remains in its original condition or position by the time it appears, say, in court. And only a person of peculiar obtuseness could fail to realise that this argument holds over much shorter periods of time as well: that is to say, the person who appears in court is not the same as the one who allegedly committed the offence which, thanks to the law's delay (an oblique reference once again to *Hamlet*), may have occurred more than a year earlier.

Perhaps you will argue that the faculty of memory provides a basis for the stability of personal identity. A feeble response, ladies and gentlemen! For of all the faculties of the mind (regrettably, one has to use such inaccurate, insubstantial and unscientific terms as *mind* if one is to speak at all), memory is the least reliable. You maintain that your personal identity is a continuous and unbroken stream since you first reached the age of consciousness, but not even the least honest among you would claim that your stream of memory since then is continuous and unbroken. Thus, your memory cannot stand guarantor of that precious identity of yours. Indeed, nothing can.

I have, of course, further objections to memory. It has been conclusively established by experimentation that people do not remember what really happened and – worse still from the point of view of your argument – claim to remember what did not happen. Eyewitnesses recall logically contradictory events; and the versions of their childhood which most people provide when asked to do so depend more upon the image of themselves they wish to project than upon what they were actually like. Memory is the means by which the past is distorted to present purposes.

But even if memory were perfectly reliable, ladies and gentlemen, it would not and could not establish the continuance of personal identity, but on the contrary its very opposite. How so, you ask? Because with each passing moment, the store of memory must be increased, its content enlarged; in short, changed. And surely I do not have to point out that difference cannot be used to establish identity.

I am not in general in favour of providing summaries or recapitulations of an argument, or of spelling out all its implications – this practice seems to me to promote mental laziness in a reader. But even less do I wish to be misunderstood: and therefore I restate the following two points:

i) The judge called my actions deliberate, when the very notion he had of deliberateness was incoherent and intellectually unviable, and therefore all the decisions he took on the basis of this notion were unreasonable, incompetent and unjust.

ii) The judge assumed that the person before him in the dock was the same person as the one who allegedly committed the so-called crimes which were the subject of the trial. But this was an elementary error, as I have demonstrated. Thus, the person sentenced to life imprisonment, with the recommendation that he never be released, was not the same person he assumed had killed the fifteen innocent (*sic*) people. Indeed, one person could not even have committed all the alleged offences. I therefore have one question for you, ladies and gentlemen: Can any greater offence to natural justice be imagined than to punish one man for the alleged crimes of another?

12

Since wickedness must be deliberate in order to be wickedness, and since no action can be deliberate, it follows, as the night the day (Polonius in *Hamlet*, Act 1, Scene 3), that wickedness is impossible.

Nevertheless, the judge said that I behaved with wickedness, without fear of being contradicted this side of eternity. He enjoyed pronouncing the word, but he did not know what he was talking about, his portentous manner and the grandeur of his wig and robe notwithstanding.

Let us suspend our disbelief in wickedness for a moment, however, and ask what the judge meant by this emotive word? Doing wrong for its own sake, perhaps you reply. But I counter-reply that no one ever behaves thus, or at least so small a number of people that it reduces the problem of wickedness to the dimensions of a rare neurological disorder, which afflicts only one in a million. Any human phenomenon so rare must be a disease, and one of minor importance.

No, I have never wanted to do wrong, but on the contrary have always tried to do my public duty, at the same time as developing my own personality to its full potential. You may, perhaps, disagree with what I considered right action, but what is incontestable is that I wished no harm. I am, after all, the final authority as to what my wishes were: and they were always honourable.

But what you actually did was wrong, you reply,

irrespective of your wishes. It is not the thought that counts.

Do I really have to go through it all again? Who is to decide what is right and what is wrong? Are there not societies whose ideas are very different from our own? In one country (to take a trivial, but nevertheless illustrative, example) it is deemed the height of bad manners to eat everything on one's plate, while in another it is regarded as insufferably rude to leave anything at all. When one has read as much history and anthropology as I, one is struck by the immense variation as to what has counted as moral conduct down the ages and across the continents. The Aztecs sacrificed thirty thousand men at a time, and thought they were doing right – indeed, it never occurred to them that they might be doing otherwise. I trust I do not have to give further examples, yet more extreme. It seems, therefore, that morality is like beauty, in the eye of the beholder, but I shall not repeat the Latin tag for fear of inducing tedium, a mental state not conducive to the rational assessment of philosophical arguments.

Certainly, morality – and therefore guilt or innocence, I might add – cannot be a mere matter of votes. If it were, some of the worst conduct in history would have to be deemed moral. And to whose vote should we attend, the victims' or the perpetrators'? Does one take the vote of the Mongol horde or of the inhabitants of Baghdad when the former sacked and destroyed it utterly? The victims' vote you cry, as if by reflex. But there is no reason to suppose that victims as a category have any special insight which makes their votes more valuable – to be counted double, say – than those of anyone else. My 'victims', on the contrary, were all, without exception, people whose whole lives were a negation of morality whereas I, the alleged malefactor, always sought, at least since childhood, to make my behaviour conform to the dictates of my conscience .

There is another way of conceiving of wickedness, however, though so subtle that I do not think the judge could have meant it this way. I refer, of course, to Socrates' view of the matter, namely that no man ever does wrong knowingly, by which he meant not that the wicked know not what they do, but that they know not the significance or the effect of what they do.

But this is not coherent either, if I may say so. Firstly, no one fully appreciates the effect of what they do: for every human action has consequences which the actor neither wished nor foresaw, or indeed could have foreseen. History furnishes us with innumerable examples of good coming from evil, and *vice versa*. Was not the Sistine Chapel raised in conditions of the utmost misery for the immense majority of the inhabitants of Rome, combined with the utter unscrupulousness and rascality of the elite? When it comes to failing to appreciate the effects of our actions, we are all in the same boat.

Furthermore, the very idea of failure to attend sufficiently to the effects of what one does is logically self-contradictory, and therefore cannot have any application in the real world. Socrates tells us that wickedness is a form of ignorance, to be overcome by mere thought and reflection: but *ex hypothesi* the wicked person is inattentive to precisely those effects of his actions which are harmful. In other words, he *knows* from where he should avert his gaze, which is to say that he is not ignorant. And then the question naturally arises as to why this man ignores the evil effects of his actions. The circle is closed: the man is wicked because he ignores the effects of his actions, and he ignores the effects of his actions because he is wicked. Nothing whatever is explained, ladies and gentlemen.

Besides, no one can accuse me of having disregarded the consequences to others of my actions: I thought about them long and hard. And I came to the conclusion that they would be wholly beneficial.

Of course, the judge worked himself up into a lather of indignation about the fact that I had killed fifteen people (as he so inaccurately supposed). I had deprived them of their lives, he said, without the slightest regard for their wishes. He waxed lyrical about the inestimable value of each human life, though he signally failed to enumerate any particular in which the lives of those he called my 'victims' were valuable. And when he spoke of the sanctity of human life, he omitted all mention of doctors withholding life-saving treatment from their patients when they (and they alone) deemed that their patients' lives were no longer worth living. Must one have attended medical school, I ask, to decide whether or not a life is worth living, and do medical students receive tuition in such matters that make doctors experts upon them, uniquely beyond the reach of the law?

And by what right did the judge wax indignant at the thought of all those 'poor innocent dupes', as he called them? What had he ever done for them during life, or for any member of their class, that he should feel so strongly about them? Certainly, he would never have met any of them socially: indeed, the only occasion he ever encountered any of their class was when they stood in the dock before him, and he sentenced them to one punishment or another (nine of my 'innocent victims' had been charged with a crime in court within the last year of their lives, and three of them had been imprisoned). To hand down prison sentences to people is hardly evidence of great solicitude for their welfare.

The concern expressed for my 'victims' (or subjects, as I prefer to call them) after their death contrasted rather strangely with the complete indifference shown towards them during their miserable lives, an indifference which, when you remember that it was universal on the part of society, accounted in large part for what they were or had become.

Society failed to educate them; society housed them in

138

conditions unfit for human habitation; society gave them no hope; society gave them no work to do and kept them on the margin of a pinched subsistence. But once they were dead, society wailed and gnashed its teeth. By what right, then, does society pronounce judgment upon me?

13

But judge me it did, and judge me it continues to do. It feels distinctly pleased with itself for having consigned me to perpetual imprisonment. 'He got his just deserts,' it says, adding, 'And now we are safe.' It thinks that merely by anathematising me it has satisfactorily demonstrated that I am anomalous and perverted, and therefore not the true product or offspring of itself.

But if I am so very abnormal, ladies and gentlemen, if society neither produced me nor has any place for me, may I enquire of you why it is that I receive at least two written declarations of love each week from women whom I have never met? And why have I received, in total, forty-seven offers of marriage, whereas before my achievements were known I received none at all, but on the contrary, women had not even noticed my existence? How many of you who read this can claim to have been so beloved of so many?

And I have received much support besides. I have received letters form several organisations agreeing with my contention that not only did I fail to receive a fair trial but that – because of the pre-trial publicity surrounding my case – it was inconceivable that I should have done so. For if any juror had known nothing of the matter beforehand, this would have demonstrated that he was so out of touch with everyday affairs that he was unfit to be a juror. If, on the other hand, he had knowledge of my case through the media of mass communication, he could not have been an unbiassed

140

participant of the trial. *Ergo*, no fair trial was, or is, possible; *ergo*, I should be released at once.

And then I received hundreds of letters in support of my struggle against the *lumpen* element in society. Insofar as I was reproached at all in these letters, it was for only having made a start and for not having gone far enough.

Finally, I should be accused of ingratitude if I failed to mention the *Free Underwood Committee* (FUC) which, unbidden by me, works on my behalf, pointing out to the public that even if I killed at all, which was not satisfactorily demonstrated at my trial because the forensic evidence was tainted by past scandals involving the laboratory, it was not for profit or pleasure, but for an ideal. At the very least I should be treated as a political prisoner.

I am not so naive, of course, as to suppose that I shall not remain in prison, and therefore I must make the best of it. The authorities have not yet noticed that the suicide rate among inmates of each prison in which I have so far been lodged has risen greatly. This is not because prisoners spontaneously prefer death to association with me: on the contrary, thanks to my superior intellect, knowledge and powers of persuasion I have managed to convince more than a few that by taking their own lives (I advise them also on the technical details) they are striking a blow against the police and the hated Prison Department.

And it is true that with each suicide the Department is made to feel official embarrassment. From my point of view, of course, I have – if I may be allowed what amounts to a pun – killed two birds with one stone (a prison sentence is known to prisoners as their bird). With each death, I have saved the taxpayer untold thousands, and therefore performed a further public service; but at the same time I have exposed the hypocrisy of society's supposed concern for the welfare of its prisoners.

How absolutely typical of the society we live in – its absurdity, its irrationality – that a man like me, whose burning and justified hatred of useless humanity led him to eliminate as much of it as he reasonably could, should be incarcerated in an institution in which the concentration of such humanity is the highest possible, namely one hundred per cent, and in the name of the safety of that useless humanity itself! But, ladies and gentlemen, I do not despair, far from it. I have been observing very closely how prisoners obtain positions as cleaners in the hospital wing of the prison. If necessary I shall act a part. And then, when I am a trusty in the hospital, I shall be near both drugs and equipment. So little done, so much to do! (Cecil Rhodes).

POSTSCRIPT

Extract from the Conclusions of the Report of the Official Enquiry by His Honour Judge Rosewood Davies Into the Death of Mr Graham Underwood at HM Prison, Southmead

iii) The Enquiry was satisfied that Mr Underwood died of stabwounds received while he was an inmate of 'S' (the Maximum Security) Wing of HMP Southmead.

iv) The Enquiry was satisfied that all the stabwounds suffered by Mr Underwood were inflicted by the inmates of 'S' Wing, and that there is no substance to the rumour that there was collusion, either active or passive, on the part of the prison officers.

v) The Enquiry found, however, that the prison officers of 'S' Wing were lacking in reasonable forethought when they permitted Mr Underwood to associate with the other inmates of 'S' Wing, who were themselves known to be dangerous and violent, and several of whom were convicted murderers, at a time when feeling against Mr Underwood in the prison was known to be running high.

vi) Moreover, there were several breaches of security regulations which allowed the inmates of 'S' Wing to procure or manufacture the weapons with which they stabbed Mr Underwood. In part, these breaches were caused by inadequate staffing levels, and the Enquiry therefore recommends that these levels be increased, and if possible doubled, in the interest of public security and the safety of inmates.

vii) Furthermore, the Enquiry found that the response

of the officers on duty in 'S' Wing at the time of the incident was inadequately coordinated, that there was a lack of proper procedure laid down in the event of such an incident, that communications with other parts of the prison were poor so that there was unnecessary delay in medical assistance reaching Mr Underwood, and that the officers on 'S' Wing were not properly trained in first aid. Mr Underwood's life might have been saved had the officers been adequately trained. The Enquiry therefore recommends that further training in first aid be given all prison officers and that steps be taken to improve communications between the various locations in the prison.